Prove It

Focusing on Mathematical Reasoning and the Pythagorean Theorem

M. Katherine Gavin

Linda Jensen Sheffield

Suzanne H. Chapin

Kendall Hunt
publishing company

ACKNOWLEDGMENTS

Math Innovations Writing Team

Authors
M. Katherine Gavin
Linda Jensen Sheffield
Suzanne H. Chapin

Project Manager
Janice M. Vuolo

Teacher Edition Team
Ann Marie Spinelli
Alice J. Gabbard
Jennifer M. MacPherson

Writing Assistants
Kathy Dorkin
Jane Paulin
Jacob J. Whitmore
Mary Elizabeth Matthews

Mathematics Editor
Kathleen G. Snook

Assessment Specialist
Nancy Anderson

Advisory Board
Jerry P. Becker
Janet Beissinger
Diane J. Briars
Ann Lawrence
Ira J. Papick

Images on cover, except for detective, used under license by Shutterstock, Inc.

Photos on pp. 3, 14, 28, 35, 53, 55 and 61 used under license by ShutterStock, Inc.

Photo on p. 54 courtesy of Giovanni Dall'Orto. Photo on p. 61 © 2010 Jupiterimages Corporation.

Kendall Hunt
publishing company

www.kendallhunt.com
Send all inquiries to:
4050 Westmark Drive
Dubuque, IA 52004-1840
1-800-542-6657

Production Date: 4/8/2011
Printed by: Hess Printing Solutions
Woodstock, Illinois
United States of America
Batch number: 42646202

Prove It:
Focusing on Mathematical Reasoning and the Pythagorean Theorem

Table of Contents

UNIT GOALS

STUDENT EDITION

Prove It! : Focusing on Mathematical Reasoning and the Pythagorean Theorem

After studying this unit, you should be able to:

- Recognize and use inductive reasoning to find patterns and make generalizations.
- Recognize and use deductive reasoning to analyze logic problems and prove theorems.
- Distinguish between inductive and deductive reasoning.
- Discover, state and prove the Pythagorean Theorem.
- Use the Pythagorean Theorem and its converse in a variety of everyday situations, including surveying.
- Find squares and square roots of numbers and recognize that these processes are inverse operations.
- Define and use irrational numbers and distinguish them from rational numbers.

Dear Student Mathematician,

In *Prove It: Focusing on Mathematical Reasoning and the Pythagorean Theorem*, you will learn about two different types of reasoning: inductive and deductive. You will also learn about the Pythagorean Theorem, which is one of the most important theorems in mathematics. In this unit you will imagine yourself in two different career roles. First, as a detective, you will explore inductive and deductive reasoning. Then, as a surveyor, you will apply the Pythagorean Theorem to real-life situations. In the first section, you will encounter many problem situations from solving mysteries to analyzing mathematical statements. You will reflect on the problem-solving process and learn about inductive and deductive reasoning that you will use in math and in life.

In this unit, you will also learn about Pythagoras and his famous theorem. You will become aware of how useful this theorem is in finding distances that would otherwise be impossible to measure. Surveyors apply this theorem often in their daily jobs. In the second and third sections, you will have an opportunity to first discover the Pythagorean Theorem just as Pythagoras and his followers did, and then show why it works using a dissection proof. Finally, you will apply this theorem to a variety of real-life situations and learn about a set of numbers called irrational numbers.

We hope you enjoy the activities and applications in this unit and that you become better mathematicians by solving interesting problems using both inductive and deductive reasoning.

Mathematically yours,
The Authors

M. Katherine Gavin   *Linda Sheffield*   *Suzanne H. Chapin*

SECTION 1

Mathematical Reasoning

Mathematicians and detectives have something in common: the ability to think logically. This means the ability to look for patterns, make generalizations, and think in a step-by-step logical manner, making sure each statement follows from the known or proven facts.

Like a detective, in the next few lessons, you will need to examine evidence, use your reasoning ability and mathematical knowledge, and come to valid conclusions.

You will be using the two types of reasoning that mathematicians call inductive and deductive. You have used both of these in the past when you looked for patterns, simplified problems, eliminated possible solutions and justified your answers. In this unit, you will become aware of the type of reasoning you are using and when each type is appropriate.

LESSON 1.1 Inductive Reasoning

 Start It Off

Julio Rivera keeps on developing a mysterious rash, so he visits Dr. Perez. Dr. Perez thinks the rash might be a food reaction. She asks Julio to keep track of the foods he eats and when the rash occurs. Here is a part of Julio's chart that shows the days on which the rash appeared. Help Dr. Perez find a solution to this problem.

Day	Breakfast	Lunch	Dinner	Rash?
Monday 12/3	toast with butter, orange juice, apple	peanut butter sandwich, milk, oatmeal cookies	hamburger, fries, strawberry milkshake	Yes
Friday 12/7	granola cereal with raisins and pecans, milk	cheese pizza with pepperoni, milk, potato chips	chicken, broccoli, baked potato, chocolate cake, iced tea	Yes
Tuesday 12/11	sesame bagel with jelly, orange juice	tuna wrap, cola	steak, carrots, green beans, brownies with walnuts, lemonade	Yes
Saturday 12/15	fried eggs with bacon, milk	lemon yogurt, a bag of peanuts, chocolate milk	beef stew, vanilla pudding, iced tea	Yes

If you were Dr. Perez, how would you advise Julio to change his diet? What problem-solving strategy did you use to figure this out?

Looking for Patterns

MATHEMATICALLY SPEAKING

▶ inductive reasoning
▶ generalization

One type of reasoning detectives and mathematicians use is called inductive reasoning. When you use inductive reasoning, you look for patterns and then make a statement about those patterns. A statement that explains a pattern is called a generalization. Inductive reasoning moves from analyzing specific examples to formulating a general rule about them.

The Start It Off example shows how a doctor acts as a detective when finding the cause of an illness. As a mathematical detective, you have been looking for patterns in numbers and shapes since first grade. In later grades, you started thinking about generalizations you could make about these patterns. This is what inductive reasoning is all about.

Patterns in Pascal's Triangle

Let's use inductive reasoning to look for patterns on a famous triangle called Pascal's Triangle.

This triangle is named after French mathematician Blaise Pascal, who lived during the seventeenth century. However, he was not the first to work with this triangular pattern of numbers. Other mathematicians including the Arabian poet Omar Khayyam, who lived in the 11th century, were also fascinated with this triangle of numbers.

Blaise Pascal

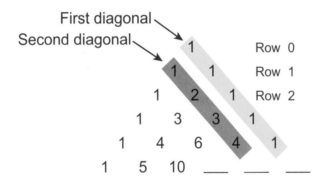

1. **a)** Fill in the blanks in the pattern above.

   b) Extend Pascal's Triangle by writing the next three lines of the pattern.

   c) Find at least four number patterns in the triangle. Describe them.

   d) Share your patterns with a partner and see if together you can find some more. How are the numbers in each row related to the numbers in the rows above and below it?

2. There are many interesting patterns in Pascal's Triangle. Investigate the pattern in the diagonals described below.

   a) Take a look at the diagonals. Notice the numbers in the first diagonal from left to right are 1, 1, 1, ... What is the 100th term in this first diagonal?

   b) When we make a generalization, we often use a variable such as n to represent any number in a sequence or pattern. What is the nth term in the first diagonal?

   c) Find the 100th term in the second diagonal from left to right. Find the nth term.

3. There are also interesting patterns in the rows of Pascal's triangle.

   a) Take a look at the rows. We call the top row, with the number 1 in it, Row 0. Find the number of terms in Row 100. Find the number of terms in Row n.

   b) How many times does the largest number appear in Row 1, Row 3, or Row 5? In any odd-number row?

   c) How many times does the largest number appear in Row 0, Row 2, or Row 4? In any even-number row?

   d) Look at the rows where the number to the right of 1 is prime. What can you say about the rest of the numbers in the row?

   Hint
   See page 123

Think Beyond

   e) Write each row as a number that you would read from left to right. For example, Row 4 would be the number 14,641. Can you find a pattern in these numbers?

   Hint
   See page 123

Think Beyond

   f) Find the sum of the numbers in each row from Row 0 through Row 3. Look for a pattern in the sums. Find the sum of the numbers in Row n.

   Hint
   See page 123

Patterns with Intersecting Lines

Look at the figures below. Each time a line is added, the number of regions created changes. For example, one line creates two regions and two lines create four regions.

4. a) Create the next figure in the pattern.

    b) A table can help you figure out patterns. Fill in the table below and find the number of regions created by 20 lines that intersect at a common point.

Number of Lines	1	2	3	4	5	20	n
Number of Regions	2	4	6				

    c) In general, how many regions are created by n lines that intersect at a common point?

Kendra's Pattern

Kendra made a pattern with popsicle sticks. She made an unusual shape using 8 popsicle sticks and then put several of these shapes together. She then removed any inside sticks to create her design.

 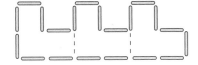 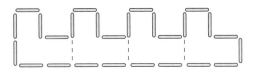

The tall parts of the figure started to look like towers, and Kendra decided to make a design with 25 towers. She wanted to figure out how many sticks she needed to create her design.

5. a) Complete Kendra's table for up to 6 towers.

Number of Towers	1	2	3	4	5	6
Number of Popsicle Sticks	8	14	20			

b) Describe the pattern to find the number of sticks from one design to the next.

 **Let's Review** The rule you just described is a **recursive rule.** A recursive rule is a rule that helps you find a new output value by using the previous result. We write this as *new = previous +* _____ . In this case, the rule is *new = previous +* 6.

c) Find the number of sticks for the 10th design by extending the table using the recursive rule.

6. a) In the table above, describe the pattern between the number of towers and the number of sticks. This will help you find the number of sticks needed for 25 towers without finding the number of sticks needed for every figure up to the 24th. Describe a rule to find the number of sticks needed for 25 towers.

 **Let's Review** The rule you just described is called the **explicit rule.** An explicit rule is a rule that relates two variables in a situation using mathematics.

b) Name the two variables in this situation.

c) Use math symbols to write an explicit rule to find the number of sticks needed to make a design. Let n = the number of towers.

d) How does your explicit rule relate to the recursive rule you found in Question 5b?

7. a) Find the number of sticks needed for a figure with 50 towers and for a figure with 112 towers.

b) Find the number of towers in a figure with 596 sticks.

c) Explain how you have used inductive reasoning in this problem.

8. a) Write the recursive and explicit rules for the intersecting lines pattern in Question 4.

b) Write the recursive and explicit rules for finding a number in the second diagonal in Pascal's triangle.

9. Create your own pattern.

   a) Create a table like the one Kendra used. The top row should be the same as Kendra's. The bottom row should be a new pattern of numbers that you create using a recursive rule. On another sheet of paper describe the pattern by writing the explicit rule in words.

   b) Trade with your partner and find the next three terms of each other's sequences. Describe your partner's pattern by writing recursive and explicit rules for it.

Arithmetic and Geometric Sequences

MATHEMATICALLY SPEAKING

▶ **arithmetic sequence**

▶ **geometric sequence**

10. Sequences that have a constant difference between consecutive terms are called arithmetic sequences. For example, the sequence 3, 5, 7, 9, ... is arithmetic since there is a constant difference of 2 between any two consecutive terms. Are there any other arithmetic sequences you have used in this lesson?

11. Write the recursive rule for each arithmetic sequence and find the next three terms.

    a) 25, 50, 75, ...

    b) 84, 79, 74, ...

    c) −1.5, −1, −0.5, ...

    d) Write the first six terms of your own arithmetic sequence.

12. In a geometric sequence, each term is multiplied by the same number to obtain the next term. For example, in the sequence 3, 9, 27, 81, ..., each term is multiplied by 3 to get the next term. Find the next three terms of each geometric sequence.

    a) 5, 10, 20, ...

    b) 8, 4, 2, ...

    c) $1, \frac{1}{4}. \frac{1}{16}, ...$

    d) Write the first six terms of your own geometric sequence.

 **Wrap It Up**

What is the difference between recursive rules and explicit rules? How are both used in inductive reasoning to make generalizations?

MATHEMATICALLY SPEAKING

▶ arithmetic sequence

▶ explicit rule

▶ generalization

▶ geometric sequence

▶ inductive reasoning

▶ recursive rule

On Your Own

MATERIALS LIST

▶ Calculator

▶ Lesson Guide 1.1:
  Pascal's Triangle

▶ Internet access

 Write About It

1. Describe the difference between recursive and explicit rules. When making generalizations, what is the advantage of using the explicit rule?

2. Describe a situation in which you used inductive reasoning that was not related to numbers or shape patterns. Explain why you think it was inductive reasoning.

3. How many regions are formed by *n* parallel lines?

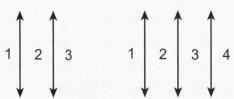

 Hint
See page 123

 **Think Beyond**

4. How many points of intersection will there be if *n* lines intersect so that no two lines are parallel to each other and no three lines intersect at the same point?

5. Jose came up with an interesting pattern and was trying to stump his brother. He asked his brother, "How many triangles are formed when you draw all possible diagonals from a single vertex of a 40-sided polygon?" His brother attempted to draw a 40-sided polygon and quickly gave up. However, there is a way to figure this out without having to draw a polygon with 40 sides. Find a pattern that will help Jose's brother.

 **Hint**
See page 123

6. Create Pascal's triangle up to Row 15 using Lesson Guide 1.2. Color the even numbers one color and the odd numbers a different color. You will be surprised! Research the Sierpinski triangle to find out some interesting information about this design.

 **Think Beyond**

7. In Rows 0 and 1 of Pascal's triangle, all numbers are odd. List the next three rows in which only odd numbers occur. Predict the next row where only odd numbers will occur. Explain why the numbers are all odd.

8. Write the first six terms of two sequences in which the third term is 9. Describe the pattern for each using the explicit rule.

9. For each problem below, fill in the missing numbers or expressions. First, find the recursive rule and use it to help you find the explicit rule.

a)

Term	1	2	3	4	5	8	10	12		n
Value	4	8	12	16					112	

The recursive rule is _____. The explicit rule is _____.

b)

Term	1	2	3	4	5	8	10	12		n
Value	3	5	7	9					37	

The recursive rule is _____. The explicit rule is _____.

c)

Term	Value
1	1
2	4
3	7
4	10
5	
8	
10	
12	
	67
n	

The recursive rule is _____. The explicit rule is _____.

10. Find the next four terms of each sequence. Is the sequence arithmetic or geometric? Explain.

   a) 15, 75, 375, …

   b) 117, 97, 77, …

   c) 12.26, 12.32, 12.38, …

   d) 18, 3.6, 0.72, …

   e) $x, x + 3, x + 6, …$

11. Explain to a friend who was absent for this lesson the difference between an arithmetic sequence and a geometric sequence. Give an example of each.

12. Something interesting happens when you compute the difference between each pair of successive terms in a geometric sequence.

   Start with the sequence 8, 4, 2, 1, … . Make a new sequence using the differences. You should get 4, 2, 1, … . It is another geometric sequence since each term is multiplied by $\frac{1}{2}$ to get the next term.

   a) Form new sequences this way using the geometric sequences in Question 12 a, c, and d in the lesson. Are the new sequences geometric? Show your work.

   b) Use inductive reasoning to make a conjecture about the sequences formed by the differences between each pair of successive terms in a geometric sequence.

 **Think Beyond**

13. Examine the explicit rules you have found for the arithmetic sequences in this lesson. Generalize your results by completing the following: If the difference between successive terms is d, and the first term is f, the rule for the nth term is _____ .

 Think Beyond

14. To create the design below, you start with the black triangle shown to the far left, and remove a triangle from its center, as shown in the second figure. Then, repeat this step with each of the newly-formed triangles to get the next figure, and so on. How many repeats of the original design can you find in the second figure? In the third figure? Look for a pattern and then predict the number of copies of the original design in the 10th figure. Find an explicit rule for the number of repetitions of the original design in the nth figure.

Think Back

15. After his rousing victory over the hare, the tortoise decides to challenge his long-time rival, the garden snail, to a race. The snail agrees to the race only if he gets a 12-hour head start. The maximum speed of the snail is 0.03 mph, and the maximum speed of the tortoise is 0.15 mph. If the race is 0.60 miles long, who wins? When the winner crosses the finish line, how far behind is the loser?

16. If I pay $24 for a shirt at a sale, and I have saved 25%, what was the original price?

17. Solve for x and show your work: $(2 + 3)x + (2 - 5) = 7$.

18. **What went wrong?** Jocelyn was trying to evaluate the expression $3 + 2(5 - 7)$. Her teacher disagreed with her answer. Help her find her error and the correct answer.

    $3 + 2(5 - 7)$

    $5(5 - 7)$

    $5(-2)$

    The answer is -10.

19. $4.01 + 0.401 + 40 =$

    A. 0.841

    B. 4.811

    C. 44.411

    D. 44.42

One Schoolboy's Discovery

➡️ Start It Off

Use inductive reasoning to look for patterns. Then draw the next design.

1. How would you describe to a friend over the phone how you figured out what the next drawing would be?

2. How many sides does the outer polygon have in each design?

3. How many line segments are in each design?

4. How many diagonals are in each design?

At School with Carl Gauss

When Carl Gauss, a famous mathematician, was a schoolboy in the 1700s in Germany, his teacher needed some time to work on her own. She instructed the class to add the whole numbers from 1 to 100. Carl had the correct answer very quickly, and his astonished teacher asked him to explain how he did it!

1. a) Without using a calculator, see how fast you can come up with this sum. (Carl would not have had access to a calculator back then!) Use inductive reasoning to help you.

    b) Share your findings with a partner. Did you both find the sum the same way?

    c) Share your method(s) with the class and compare results.

Carl Gauss

Maybe you thought about simplifying the problem. This is an excellent problem-solving strategy. Examine the sums 1, 1 + 2, 1 + 2 + 3, and 1 + 2 + 3 + 4, and look for a pattern. Let's see how this method works

2. a) Complete the table below. Look for patterns and state the recursive rule.

Number of Addends	1	2	3	4	5	6	7	8
Summing Expression	1	1 + 2	1 + 2 + 3					
Sum	1	3	6					

b) How is the sum pattern in this problem different from the patterns we found in the last lesson?

Take a look at the clever way young Carl found the sum. To simplify the problem, we will stop at 10 instead of 100. To figure out how Carl did this, write down the numbers from 1 to 10 and then from 10 to 1 as shown below. Then add each column.

3. a) Talk to your partner. How do you think this might help find the sum of the numbers from 1 to 10? Think about the following:

- How is the number 11 related to the number 10?

- Find the sum of the bottom row. How many times did you add the number 11?

- Now find the sum of the numbers from 1 to 10 using your calculator.

- How are the two sums related?

b) Write a rule in words that can be used to find the sum of the numbers from 1 to 10.

c) Use your rule to find some other sums and see if you can find patterns.

d) Find the sum from 1 to 100 using the pattern you found.

e) Write a rule that you can use to find the sum of the first *n* consecutive numbers.

Hint
See page 123

f) Use your rule to add the first 6 counting numbers, the first 8 counting numbers, and the first 12 counting numbers. Check your answer by finding these sums with a calculator.

4. Use this rule to help you find the following sums:

   a) $2 + 3 + 4 + 5 + 6 + 7 + 8 + \ldots + 15$

   b) $11 + 12 + 13 + \ldots + 100$

Triangular Numbers

5. a) Find the next two shapes in the pattern below and explain how you determined these shapes.

Shape 1   Shape 2   Shape 3

The numbers associated with these shapes are called triangular numbers. Why do you think they have this name?

   b) How are these numbers related to what you have studied in this lesson so far?

   c) What is the 12th triangular number? What is the 20th triangular number?

6. a) Write a recursive rule for generating the triangular numbers.

   b) Write an explicit rule for generating the triangular numbers.

7. Where is the triangular number pattern found in Pascal's triangle?

In 1796, Carl Gauss made a very interesting mathematical discovery. He found that every positive integer can be written as the sum of at most three triangular numbers. He wrote in his diary, "Eureka! Num = $\Delta + \Delta + \Delta$." For example, $56 = 55 + 1$, $20 = 10 + 10$, and $113 = 91 + 21 + 1$.

8. Write the integers from 1 to 10 as the sum of at most three triangular numbers.

9. There are many interesting patterns found in triangular numbers. Use inductive reasoning to look for patterns that will help you fill in the blanks for the generalization stated below.

   The sum of two consecutive triangular numbers is always a

   _____.

10. Have you ever heard of Harshad numbers? A Harshad number is an integer that is divisible by the sum of its digits. Harshad numbers were defined by D. R. Kaprekar, a mathematician from India. The word "Harshad" comes from the Sanskrit (an ancient language of India), *harṣa*, meaning "great joy."

    For example, 111 is a Harshad number since the sum of its digits, $1 + 1 + 1$, equals 3 and $111 \div 3 = 37$, so 111 is divisible by 3.

    Find the first eight Harshad triangular numbers.

11. The Marks are having a family reunion. Everyone is coming, including Grandma and Grandpa, Uncle Bob, Cousin Monica, and even granddaughter, Kayleigh. In all, there are a total of 82 people attending. If each person hugs every other person, how many hugs will go around on the day of the family reunion?

    a) Talk to your partner about a good problem-solving strategy.

    b) Find the explicit rule for the number of hugs when n people are at the reunion.

    c) How does this rule compare to the rule for the sum of consecutive integers?

Wrap It Up

Create a new problem. Use your problem to show how mathematicians use inductive reasoning to come up with generalizations. Share your problem with your partner and then with the class.

MATERIALS LIST

▶ Calculator

▶ Lesson Guide 1.2:
Diagonals to Skateboard By

Write About It

1. **a)** Explain what inductive reasoning is and how it is used to find the sum of the numbers from 1 to 100.

   b) Write a general rule to find the sum of any set of consecutive numbers.

   c) Is your rule an explicit or a recursive rule? Explain your answer.

2. Use the rule for the sum of any set of consecutive numbers to find the following:

   a) the sum of the first 50 counting numbers

   b) the sum of the first 500 positive integers

3. Use the rule for the sum of any set of consecutive numbers to find the sums below:

   a) $3 + 4 + 5 + \dots + 20$

   b) $10 + 11 + 12 + \dots + 100$

   c) $5 + 6 + 7 \dots + 200$

   d) Explain how you used the rule to get the answer.

4. **a)** Find the total number of bricks in a pyramid that has 10 bricks in the bottom row. Here is a picture of a smaller version to start you off.

   b) What is the total if the bottom row has 75 bricks?

   c) How does this problem relate to Gauss' rule?

5. For each table below, fill in the missing number or expression, and state the recursive and explicit rules.

a)

Term	1	2	3	4	5	8	10	n
Value	$\frac{1}{2}$	1	$1\frac{1}{2}$	2				

The recursive rule is _____. The explicit rule is _____.

b)

Term	Value
1	3
2	5
3	7
4	9
5	
6	
n	

The recursive rule is _____. The explicit rule is _____.

c)

Term	1	2	3	4	5		25	n
Value	0	3	6	9		27		

The recursive rule is _____. The explicit rule is _____.

6. Find the pattern and the missing number or symbol for the circles or the triangles.

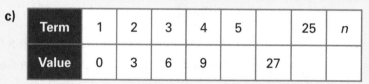

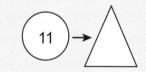

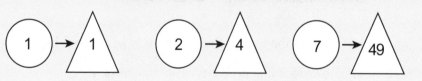

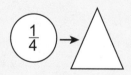

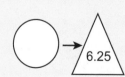

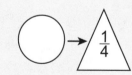

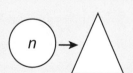

7. Use inductive reasoning to fill in the tables and find the explicit rules.

a)

Term	1	2	3	4	5	8	10	12		n
Value	$\frac{1}{2}$	$\frac{1}{6}$	$\frac{1}{12}$	$\frac{1}{20}$					$\frac{1}{420}$	

The explicit rule is _____.

b)

Term	1	2	3	4	5	6	10	n		
Value	0	3	8	15	24					

The explicit rule is _____.

8. Here is an interesting number array made by an eighth grader. See if you can answer the questions about it using inductive reasoning.

```
        1 ◄──── Row 1
      1  2  1
    1  2  3  2  1
  1  2  3  4  3  2  1
```

a) Continue the pattern for the next two rows.

b) What are the middle terms in Rows 8, 20, and 65? What is the middle term in Row n?

c) What are the 10th terms in Rows 10, 12, 88, 8 and 6?

d) What is the sum of the terms in Row 1? Row 2? Row 3? Row 10? Row 26?

Come up with a generalization in words for finding the sum of any row. Write an explicit rule for the sum of the terms in Row n.

e) What is the number of terms in the array up to and including Row 3? Row 4? Row 12? Row 30? Explain your generalization in words and with an explicit rule using variables.

9. **Diagonals to Skateboard By**

Jose's brother told him that if he could figure out the number of diagonals in a 33-sided polygon, he would let him use his skateboard for a week. Help Jose find the answer.

a) Use the shapes below and figure out the number of diagonals in a 33-sided polygon.

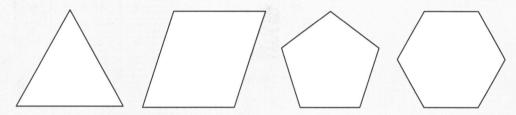

b) Find the explicit rule. Use the Student Lesson Guide "Diagonals To Skateboard By" to help you organize your thinking.

Think Beyond

10. Nikesha and Rebecca are having fun making towers out of 1-inch cubes. They create an interesting design that looks like a pyramid with steps up to the top from four different directions. They build pyramids that are one layer high (just one block), two layers and so on. They want to build a pyramid that is 25 layers high. What is the total number of blocks they will need? Use a table and your inductive reasoning skills to find an explicit rule for the total number of blocks in a pyramid with *n* layers.

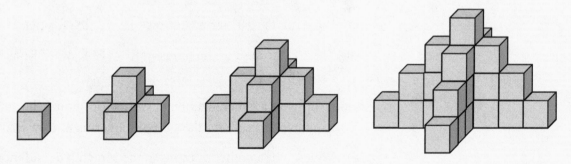

11. Water drips from Anna's sink faucet at the rate of 80 drops per minute. At this rate, how many times does it drip in half an hour?

A. 1,600   C. 4,000

B. 2,400   D. 4,800

12. **What went wrong?** Tiana paid $12 for a T-shirt that was on sale for 15% off the regular price. She wanted to find out the regular price and did the following calculations. Her answer doesn't make sense. Figure out what went wrong and find the original price.

12 = 15% of _____.

12 ÷ 0.15 = 80   The original price of the T-shirt was $80.

13. To celebrate his birthday, Carlos decides to buy a pint of ice cream. The day he buys it, he eats one-fifth of it. The next day, he eats one-fourth of the remaining ice cream. How much ice cream does Carlos have left? Express your answer as both a fraction and as a percentage of the original pint.

14. $1 - \frac{4}{3} + \frac{3}{4} =$ _____. Show your work.

15. If I take out all the jacks and kings from a standard deck of cards, and then draw one card from the deck that remains, what is the probability that I will draw a red 10 out? What is the probability I will draw a black card?

Take Caution with Inductive Reasoning

➡ Start It Off

1. What comes next?

Kalina drew this picture to answer the question.

Ty drew this picture to answer the question.

Their teacher said that both could be correct! Explain how they might have used inductive reasoning to come up with their answers, and describe their pattern or rule.

2. How might a student use inductive reasoning to come up with the following generalizations? Do you agree with the generalization? Explain your answer.

   a) Girls like to cook more than boys do.

   b) The taller a person is, the larger his or her shoe size is.

Multiple Patterns

1. **a)** Find the next numbers in this sequence.

1, 2, 4, _____, _____, _____

b) Jenna came up with 8, 16 and 32 as the next numbers in the sequence. What rule did she use?

c) Cory came up with 7, 11 and 16. What rule did he use?

d) Based on Cory's rule, what would the next two numbers be?

e) When you use inductive reasoning you may come up with more than one correct conclusion, depending on the pattern you recognize. Why do you think it happened in this example?

2. **a)** Create a new number sequence so that that there is more than one possible value for the fourth term. Write the first three terms in the sequence.

b) Trade with a partner and see if you can find more than one way to continue your partner's sequence.

Patterns that Don't Continue

In some instances inductive reasoning can lead us down a path that gives a wrong answer because the pattern does not continue to hold.

> *It never rains in Aruba...* *That's what the travel brochure says. Excited about this, you go on vacation to Aruba, and it is sunny and hot the first five days. On the sixth day, thinking it will again be sunny and hot, you head to the beach for a picnic lunch. But, a half-hour into your picnic, the rain comes pouring down.*

In this situation, you used inductive reasoning. You figured that since the past five days were sunny, this same weather would continue. But, no such luck!

3. Talk with your partner and come up with another real-world situation in which using inductive reasoning can lead to a wrong conclusion.

Inductive reasoning can sometimes lead us down the wrong path in mathematics too.

4. We know that $10 > 9$.

$10 \cdot 8 > 9 \cdot 8$ *true*

$10 \cdot 7 > 9 \cdot 7$ *true*

$10 \cdot 6 > 9 \cdot 6$ *true*

a) Continue the pattern to write the next three inequalities. Use inductive reasoning to make a generalization about multiplying both sides of an inequality by the same number. Share your generalizations with the class.

b) Now write the next four inequalities. Does your generalization still hold true? Why or why not?

MATHEMATICALLY SPEAKING

▶ counterexample

You have just witnessed the power of the counterexample. A counterexample is an example that contradicts a generalization made from previous examples and shows that the generalization is false.

5. Give an additional counterexample that shows the generalization made in Question 4 does not hold true.

A Magic Trick

Let's see how to use inductive reasoning to make a generalization about a magic trick.

6. Try this number trick.
Pick your favorite number.
Add 4. Multiply by 2. Subtract 8.
Subtract your original number.
What is your answer?

a) Compare your results with a partner and then with the class.

b) Make a generalization.

c) Can you find a counterexample? If not, does this mean the trick will always work?

To prove this generalization is always true, you would need to check every possible example or use variables to show how it works for any number. More to come!!

 # Wrap It Up

Inductive reasoning is helpful in giving us ideas about what may occur, but it cannot be used to prove anything for certain. Explain how the generalizations made using inductive reasoning can sometimes be disproven.

Write About It

1. Why is it impossible to show that a generalization is true by checking using examples?

2. Describe a real-life situation in which the generalizations that might be made can be disproven.

3. You know that inductive reasoning cannot prove that generalizations are always true. The students in Mr. Spinelli's class were exploring patterns with integers and came up with the following generalizations using inductive reasoning. If possible, find a counterexample that contradicts each generalization.

   a) The square of an integer is always greater than the integer itself.

   b) All prime numbers are odd.

   c) The sum of any three consecutive integers is divisible by 3.

   d) Any integer divisible by 6 is also divisible by 12.

   e) The product of an odd integer and an even integer is always even.

   f) Subtracting a negative integer from any integer will result in a difference that is negative.

4. Write a counterexample that would disprove each of these generalizations:

   a) A movie made from a book is never as good as the book itself.

   b) On any given day, it is warmer in Florida than it is in Connecticut.

   c) Big dogs bark less than little dogs.

5. Write two generalizations that seem reasonable. At least one of your statements must be able to be contradicted with a counterexample. Trade statements with your partner. Use inductive reasoning to list examples that seem to indicate that the statements your partner wrote are true. If possible, find counterexamples.

Think Beyond

6. **It's Magic!** Pick a number and add 12. Multiply by 2. Subtract 10. Now subtract your original number. What happens? Try several numbers and make a generalization. Show why your generalization is true and works for any number.

7. Make up your own magic trick involving numbers and operations. Try it out with your friends and family. Make sure you can prove it works for all numbers.

8. If today is Thursday, 30 days from today will be which day of the week? How do you know?

9. For the integers from 1 up to and including 10, what is the ratio of the number of even numbers to the number of odd numbers? Using the same set of numbers, what is the ratio of the number of prime numbers to the number of numbers divisible by 2?

10. What number is halfway between 2 and –10 _____? Show this on a number line.

11. **What went wrong?** Maria bought a dress that originally cost $60. She saw a sign that said all prices will be reduced by 20% and she also had a coupon that gave her 10% off.

    She added 20% + 10% = 30% and then figured that 0.30 • $60 = $18. She subtracted 60 − 18 and got her final cost as $42.

    Figure out her error and find the correct price.

12. $\frac{8}{9} \cdot 72 =$

    A. 64

    B. 81

    C. 648

    D. 576

Deductive Reasoning

 Start It Off

The Robbery at the Avon Hotel

As head detective, your job is to determine who committed the crime. Here is what you know so far:

- The robber stayed at the hotel on the night of the crime.

- The robber escaped by diving from the fourth floor balcony into the Farmington River and then swimming away.

- Black hair from the robber was found on the railing of the second floor balcony.

- Smudges were found on the glass coffee table indicating that the robber wore gloves.

You have five suspects. Based on the following information, who is most likely to be the robber?

- Big Bobby Black is 200 cm tall and weighs 100 kg. He has never spent a night away from his home in Bakersville, a town about 10 km away from the hotel.

- Yetti Yellow is an airline pilot who frequently stays at the hotel.

- Rooster Red is a small man who stands about 160 cm tall. He is nicknamed Rooster because of his rooster-like strut. He is petrified of high places and refuses to even climb a ladder.

- Georgia Gray is a maid who works at the hotel and was on duty the day of the robbery.

- Curly White earns his nickname because of his completely bald head.

You have seen how inductive reasoning helps you find patterns and general rules. You have also learned that this type of reasoning has its limitations. In fact, for every situation, one counterexample is all it takes to show the pattern or rule is not true.

Deductive reasoning is another type of reasoning that mathematicians use to prove something is true beyond a doubt. In deductive reasoning, you use a logical step-by-step argument from statements that are accepted as true or have been proven to be true.

Detectives also use deductive reasoning. Police detectives would use the process of elimination as you just did to solve the robbery at the Avon Hotel.

The Process of Elimination

The strategy of eliminating possibilities one by one is an example of deductive reasoning. Let's use the process of elimination in working with geometric shapes. We are going to play a game called *Guess My Shape*.

GAME · · · · · Guess My Shape · · · · ·

Players: 2–4

Materials: One set of Attribute Blocks per group

DIRECTIONS:

- Groups of 2–4 students get a set of blocks. These blocks differ *in size, shape, color, and width.*

- The leader will think of one specific block for the rest of the class to guess.

- Each group will have a turn to ask a question that can be answered by "yes" or "no," or to actually make a guess of which block it is.

- To win the game, you have to state the specific block in terms of shape, size, and color (and width, if applicable).

1. Play the game with your teacher as leader first, and then in groups with different students taking turns being the leader.

2. Use the process of elimination to solve this mystery number puzzle.

   Clue 1: I am a two-digit number.

   Clue 2: I am the first integer to the right of a palindrome on the number line.

   **Hint**
   See page 123

   Clue 3: The sum of my digits is 15.

   **Hint**
   See page 123

Who am I?

3. Talk to your partner and discuss how deductive reasoning with the process of elimination were used in figuring out:

   a) which shape the person was thinking of in **Guess My Shape.**

   b) the mystery number.

Figure It Out!

You can also use the process of elimination to help you solve different kinds of puzzles.

4. WOMEN AT WORK

Flora, Rosa, Belle and Electra are women who love their jobs (engineer, horticulturalist, gardener, symphony conductor). From the clues to the right match up each woman's name with her work.

Clue 1: Flora is very allergic to most plants.

Clue 2: Rosa and the horticulturalist are roommates.

Clue 3: Rosa likes only country music.

Clue 4: The gardener, the engineer, and Electra do not know each other.

Use the following chart to help you solve the puzzle. For example, from the first clue we know that Flora cannot be the horticulturalist or the gardener. So we put an "X" in each of those two boxes.

	Engineer	Horticulturalist	Gardener	Symphony Conductor
Flora		X	X	
Rosa				
Belle				
Electra				

5. SERVING OTHERS

The last names of Paul, Sophie and Brittany are Robson, Stuckey and Jones, not necessarily in that order. Each person volunteers at one of the following organizations: the Red Cross, The Friends in Need homeless shelter, and Children's Hospital Boston. Find each person's full name and the place at which they volunteer.

Clue 1: The Friends in Need volunteer said he serves about 100 meals each week.

Clue 2: Robson likes working at the Red Cross but wishes Sophie would also volunteer there.

Clue 3: Jones does not work at a homeless shelter.

Use the table below. The first clue tells you that the homeless shelter volunteer is male. Since Paul is the only male, put an "O" (indicating a "yes" response) in the cell that corresponds to "Paul" and "Friends in Need." You can now put an X in the boxes underneath the O in the "Friends in Need" column since we know Paul is the volunteer here. Using the process of elimination, mark an "X" in the cells that would indicate Paul could be the hospital volunteer or the Red Cross volunteer.

	Robson	Stuckey	Jones	Red Cross	Friends in Need	Children's Hospital Boston
Paul				X	O	X
Sophie					X	
Brittany					X	
Red Cross						
Friends in Need						
Children's Hospital Boston						

6. CAT SHOW

There was a cat show at the Convention Center. There were four prizes: gold, silver, bronze and pewter lined up next to each other in this order on a table. The prize winners, a Siamese, a tabby, a Persian and an Abyssinian cat all wore collar tags of different colors. Find the tag color of each cat and the prize won by each cat. (There were no ties for prizes.)

Clue 1: The Siamese wore a blue collar tag and not an orange tag.

Clue 2: The tabby received the prize that was next to the cat with the brown collar tag.

Clue 3: The cat with the yellow collar tag won the gold prize.

Clue 4: The cat with the brown collar tag won the silver prize.

Clue 5: The colors of the collar tags of the Siamese and the Abyssinian mix to form green.

Hint
See page 123

	Gold	Silver	Bronze	Pewter	Yellow	Brown	Blue	Orange
Siamese								
Tabby								
Persian								
Abyssinian								

				Gold
				Silver
				Bronze
				Pewter

Wrap It Up

Explain what the process of elimination is and how you would use it to find a solution to a problem similar to the ones in the lesson.

MATHEMATICALLY SPEAKING

▶ deductive reasoning

MATERIALS LIST

► *Agatha Christie:
An Autobiography*
(optional for Think
Beyond)

 **Write
About It**

1. How are inductive and deductive reasoning
alike? How are they different?

2. **a)** Find the Mystery Number and explain your answer.

   Clue 1 The sum of the digits of this two-digit number is 11.

   Clue 2 The tens digit is larger than the ones digit.

   Clue 3 The number is one more than a prime number.

 **Think
Beyond**

   b) Write hints for one or two clues that will help students use the
   process of elimination.

3. The women's basketball team at Yukon College was on the road
   playing in Montana and checked into the Husky Hotel. One of the
   team members, Kara, was unpacking gear from the bus while the
   others checked in. Her roommate, who loved math games, handed Kara
   the access card to her room, but decided to make her guess the room
   number. What is Kara's room number? Here are the clues:

   Clue 1 The hotel was three stories high and all room numbers had
   3 digits that start with the floor number.

   ? Hint
   See page 123

   Clue 2 Each of the digits in Kara's room number is a different
   prime number and the middle digit in Kara's room number
   is the smallest prime.

   Clue 3 The difference between any two of the digits in Kara's room
   number is not greater than 4.

   ? Hint
   See page 123

4. Miguel and Rosa just came back from a Halloween party. Miguel said to Rosa, "I bet you can't guess the number of candy bars I have in my sack." Rosa said, "Well, give me some clues."

What is Rosa's answer?

5. Keisha found a piece of paper with clues to a number riddle. The only problem was that the last clue was torn off. With the clues that are given, there is more than one answer.

   a) Find all the possible answers using the given clues.

   b) Make up a new clue that will give only one number as the correct answer. If you want to be clever, make the last clue rhyme with the clue above so the poem continues.

Solve the Number Riddle

● Clue 1   A positive integer am I.

Clue 2   My three digits are different and odd, don't know why.

● Clue 3   When you add them together, their sum is a perfect square.

Clue 4

6. What's your favorite number? Make up some clues similar to the ones on page 34. Try it out with a partner or someone at home to make sure your clues work. (Did you eliminate all possibilities but one? If not, revise your clues or add another so that your answer is a unique number.)

7. Tony, Mike, Sandra and Maria, whose last names are Casa, Ortez, Partino and Lewis, live in Connecticut, Massachusetts, Alabama and Indiana. Use the clues in the detective's notebook to help Detective McDermott match each first name with a last name and state.

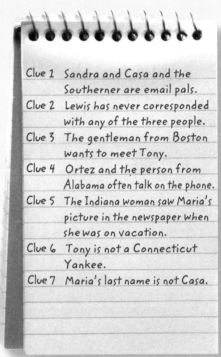

Clue 1 Sandra and Casa and the Southerner are email pals.

Clue 2 Lewis has never corresponded with any of the three people.

Clue 3 The gentleman from Boston wants to meet Tony.

Clue 4 Ortez and the person from Alabama often talk on the phone.

Clue 5 The Indiana woman saw Maria's picture in the newspaper when she was on vacation.

Clue 6 Tony is not a Connecticut Yankee.

Clue 7 Maria's last name is not Casa.

8. Bonnie, Bill, Barbara and Ben each have two jobs. The jobs are chef, accountant, nurse, telephone operator, security guard, waiter, teacher and professional wrestler. Use the clues in Detective McDermott's notebook to figure out each person's two jobs.

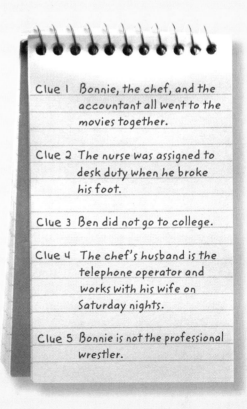

Clue 1 Bonnie, the chef, and the accountant all went to the movies together.

Clue 2 The nurse was assigned to desk duty when he broke his foot.

Clue 3 Ben did not go to college.

Clue 4 The chef's husband is the telephone operator and works with his wife on Saturday nights.

Clue 5 Bonnie is not the professional wrestler.

Think Beyond

9. To find out how a great mystery writer uses deductive reasoning, you might enjoy reading Agatha Christie's memoirs in *Agatha Christie: An Autobiography*, which she wrote over a period of fifteen years.

Think Back

10. If I live 8 miles from school, how fast do I need to ride my bike to get to school in 40 minutes? Give your answer in miles per hour.

11. Sam searches the world for buttons. No one knows why, exactly, but he does. This month he found 24 buttons each week and ended up with 367 buttons at the end of the month. How many buttons did he start the month with? (Assume there are four weeks this month.)

12. $4.7 - 0.39 =$

   A. 0.8

   B. 4.31

   C. 4.41

   D. 5.06

13. **What went wrong?** Jonathan was trying to compute the answer to $5\frac{1}{2} \div 6\frac{3}{5}$. His steps are listed below. Help Jonathan figure out his mistake.

$$5\frac{1}{2} \div 6\frac{3}{5}$$
$$\frac{11}{2} \div \frac{33}{5}$$
$$\frac{2}{11} \div \frac{33}{5}$$
$$\frac{2}{1} \cdot \frac{3}{5} = \frac{6}{5} = 1\frac{1}{5}$$

14. If you are one-third the age of your father, your father is 60% of the age of your grandfather, and your grandfather is 70, how old are you?

That's Logical!

Start It Off

Jim, Jorge and Marivalda live next to each other in the same apartment building. They have the following jobs, but not necessarily in the order given: school principal, newspaper editor and TV newscaster.

- Donna has the apartment in the middle.

- The TV newscaster feeds Jim's cat when he goes away on trips.

- The newspaper editor taps on Jim's wall when the TV is too loud.

What occupation does each person have?

In the previous lesson, you used deductive reasoning with the process of elimination. You systematically ruled out all the possibilities until there was only one left. Deductive reasoning is all about logical thinking. In deductive reasoning you demonstrate that if certain statements are true, other statements follow from them.

Thinking Logically

1. Use deductive reasoning to put the following statements in the best logical order so that each statement follows from the previous one. You should assume only what is absolutely necessary. In other words, do not add anything to the story.

I. Late for School

a) Julie gets ready for school.

b) Julie falls down a flight of steps.

c) Julie sprays hairspray in her eye.

d) Julie breaks her leg.

e) Julie needs crutches to walk.

Correct Order: _____, _____, _____, _____, _____

II. At the Bank

a) A man works as a bank teller.

b) A woman works as a bank teller.

c) A woman gives notice that she is quitting her job.

d) A woman is offered a new job.

e) A man is offered a new job.

Correct Order: _____, _____, _____, _____, _____

Share your reasoning and your answers with a partner. If your answers are not the same, agree on the most logical order.

2. In mathematics, we also use deductive reasoning when we think logically and make conclusions based on the given facts. Here's one example.

a) We know by definition that all quadrilaterals have four sides. Given that a rhombus is a quadrilateral, what can you conclude? Share your answer with a partner and come to an agreement.

Draw conclusions for the following:

b) Every rectangle has four right angles. A square is a rectangle.

Therefore, _____.

c) A prime number is a number with only two distinct factors, 1 and itself. 131 is a prime number.

Therefore, _____.

d) Melita is taller than Maria. Maria is taller than Maritza.

Therefore, _____.

Mathematical Proof

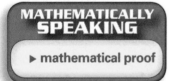

Deductive reasoning comes in handy when we want to prove in no uncertain terms that a statement is true. A mathematical proof is a logical demonstration that uses mathematical rules, properties and facts to show that a statement must be true.

Let's prove that the sum of the measures of the angles of a quadrilateral equals 360°.

In this proof, as the first step, we will use the accepted fact (we will prove this later in the year) that the sum of the measures of the angles of a triangle is 180°.

Step 1. Any quadrilateral can be divided into two triangles by drawing one diagonal within the shape.

Step 2. The sum of the angles of a triangle is 180°.

Step 3. Therefore the sum of the angles in any quadrilateral is 2(180°), or 360°.

In this proof we used deductive reasoning by starting with an accepted general statement (any quadrilateral can be divided into two triangles) and then using proven or accepted facts to come to the conclusion.

Notice that each statement uses the statement above. We could also have written this proof in paragraph format, but numbering the steps reinforces the logical reasoning.

3. Fill in the blanks in the proof below.

 **Let's Review**   Angle 1 is an interior angle of the triangle and angle 2 is the exterior angle of the triangle at the same vertex.

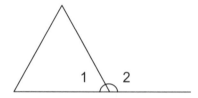

Prove that the sum of the measures of the exterior angles of an equilateral triangle equal 360°.

Step A. The sum of the measures of the interior angles of a triangle is 180°.

Step B. Each interior angle of an equilateral triangle has the same measure.

Step C. Therefore, each interior angle of an equilateral triangle measures _____.

Step D. An exterior angle and an interior angle of a triangle at the same vertex form a straight angle.

Step E. A straight angle measures _____.

Step F. Therefore, the sum of the measures of an interior and exterior angle of a triangle at the same vertex is _____.

Step G. Therefore, the exterior angle at each vertex of an equilateral triangle is _____.

Step H. Therefore, the sum of the measures of the three exterior angles of an equilateral triangle is _____.

4. Fill in the blanks.

Prove that the sum of the two acute angles of a right triangle must equal 90°.

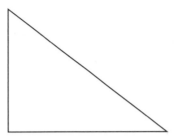

Step A.   The sum of the three angles of a right triangle is

_____.

Step B.   The right angle in a right triangle measures _____.

Step C.   By subtracting, _____ − _____ =

_____.

Step D.   Therefore, the sum of the two acute angles of a right triangle must equal _____.

We can also prove statements from algebra. Let's consider the definition of even numbers.

We know that any whole number multiplied by 2 is even. Using algebraic notation, an even number is represented by $2 \cdot a$ where a is a member of the set $\{0, 1, 2, 3,...\}$.

So if a is an element of the set $\{0, 1, 2, 3...\}$ then $2 \cdot a$ is an element of the set $\{0, 2, 4, 6,...\}$ which is the set of even numbers.

5. Using the definition of even number, fill in the blanks.

Prove that the sum of two even numbers is always even.

Step A.   Let $2a$ represent one even number and $2b$ represent another even number, where a and b are whole numbers.

Step B.   Using the _____ property, $2a + 2b = 2($_____ + _____$)$.

Step C. $2(a + b)$ is an even number. This is true because

_____.

Step D.   Therefore, the sum of any two even numbers is

_____.

 **Wrap It Up**

Jonas wanted to prove that the sum of any two negative numbers is also a negative number. He listed the following examples:

$^-16 + (^-18) = ^-34$ $^-2307 + (^-3801) = ^-6108$

$^-0.67 + (^-5.86) = ^-6.53$ $^-23.91 + (^-72.68) = ^-96.59$

$^-\frac{1}{2} + ^-\frac{1}{2} = ^-1$ $^-\frac{2}{3} + ^-1\frac{2}{3} = ^-2\frac{1}{3}$

He told Jennifer that he was convinced this was true since he had added different types of numbers such as integers, decimals, and fractions. Jennifer was not convinced.

a) Is he using inductive reasoning or deductive reasoning?

b) Did he prove that this statement is correct? Explain.

c) What would need to be done to prove his statement true? What about disproving his statement?

 **Write About It**

1. What is deductive reasoning?

2. What is the difference between inductive and deductive reasoning?

3. Either prove or disprove Jonas' statement that when we add any two negative numbers the result is negative. Explain what type of reasoning you are using to justify your answer.

? Hint
See page 123

4. Fill in the blanks below.

   a) Any whole number can be written as a fraction. Zero is a whole number.

   Therefore, _____.

   b) If a number can be written in the form 2n, where n is an integer, then the number is even. Zero can be written as 2 • 0.

   Therefore, _____.

   c) The square of an odd integer is odd. 9 is an odd integer.

   Therefore, _____.

   d) All multiples of 10 are also multiples of 5. 60 is a multiple of 10.

   Therefore, _____.

5. Put the following statements in the best logical order so that each statement follows from the previous. You should assume only what is absolutely necessary.

   I. The Break In

   a) The man proclaimed innocence to the judge.

   b) The crow bar was found next to the open safe.

   c) The family safe was found broken open in the library.

   d) A man was taken into custody.

   e) Fingerprints were traced.

II. The Morning Commute

   a) Passengers complained because the bus was late.

   b) A woman lost her job.

   c) The commuter bus started its route late.

   d) An alarm clock failed to go off.

   e) A woman was late for work.

    **Hint**
   See page 123

6. Use inductive reasoning to form a generalization about whether or not the sum of any two consecutive positive integers is even or odd.

    **Hint**
   See page 123

 **Think Beyond**

7. Write a deductive proof for the generalization you formed in Question 6.

8. Nicholas has a new magic trick he wants to share with his friends.

Think of a one-digit counting number, add 5 to it, and then multiply your answer by 3. Remember this number. Now multiply your original number by 3 and add 15. Both times you get the same answer!

Carlita tries it out. She picks 7, adds 5, and gets 12. She multiplies this by 3 and gets 36. Then she starts again with 7, multiplies it by 3, and gets 21. She then adds 15 to this and gets 36. It works!

   a) Will this work for any one-digit counting number?

    **Hint**
   See page 123

   b) What type of reasoning did you use? Explain.

   c) Show how your answer demonstrates whether or not this trick will work for a number with any number of digits.

 **Think Beyond**

9. Write a deductive proof to prove that the sum of three consecutive integers is a multiple of 3.

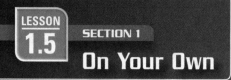

Think Back

10. Sarah has a part-time job knitting for a local shop. She is paid $13 for each hat she knits. How much does she make for knitting seven hats? How many hats does she have to knit before she has at least $50?

11. Put these in order from least to greatest.

$\frac{3}{16}$, 0.9, $\frac{5}{7}$, $\frac{1}{8}$, 0.45, $\frac{7}{9}$

12. According to Dolbear's Law, a cricket's chirps are related to the temperature as follows:

$$T = 50 + \left(\frac{N - 40}{4}\right)$$

In this formula, T = temperature in degrees Fahrenheit and N = number of cricket chirps per minute.

a) If the cricket chirps at 60 chirps per minute, what is the temperature?

b) How many chirps would the cricket make per minute if the temperature is 75° F?

13. Timothy is buying some red and blue marbles. He wants to make sure he has exactly three times more blue marbles than red. Each blue marble costs 17 cents, and each red marble costs 25 cents. How many marbles can he buy for $5.00?

14. If George can row a boat at 250 meters per minute, how long will it take him to row 3 kilometers?

Optional Technology Lesson for this section available in your eBook

Sum It Up

In this section you learned about two types of reasoning used by mathematicians and detectives. The important ideas from this section are summarized below:

Inductive Reasoning

■ Inductive reasoning is a process of making a generalization based on an observed pattern. To do this, you look for patterns in the examples that are presented. Inductive reasoning is often used to generate sequences.

■ Using inductive reasoning we can look at a sequence of numbers, determine a possible pattern, and then develop rules to explain it.

- An arithmetic sequence is a sequence of numbers in which there is a constant difference between consecutive terms. For example, the sequence 1, 5, 9, 13, ... is arithmetic since there is a constant difference of 4 between the terms.

- A geometric sequence is a sequence of numbers in which each term is multiplied by the same number to obtain the next term. For example, in the sequence 7, 21, 63, 189, …, each term is multiplied by 3 to get the next term.

- A recursive rule explains how to find the next term in a sequence by performing operations on the previous term. For example, in the sequence, 5, 10, 15, 20..., the recursive rule is adding 5 to the previous term. An explicit rule explains how to find any term (the nth term) in a sequence. For example, in the sequence, 5, 10, 15, 20... , the explicit rule is $5n$, where n represents any term of the sequence.

- A counterexample is an example that proves that a generalization is false. It takes only one counterexample to show that a statement is false.

Deductive Reasoning

MATHEMATICALLY
SPEAKING

▶ metacognition

■ Deductive reasoning is a process in which you start with accepted facts in order to prove another statement. We reason deductively when we use the process of elimination and when we demonstrate a proof by putting true statements in logical order to lead to a valid conclusion.

■ In solving logic problems, we collect all known facts and then use deductive reasoning and the process of elimination to arrive at a solution.

Many people do not consider how they think! But that is exactly what you did in this section. Thinking about our own thinking is called metacognition. It is a very powerful way to understand how to use the strategies and skills we learn and apply them to new situations.

MATHEMATICALLY SPEAKING

Do you know what these mathematical terms mean?

▶ arithmetic sequence	▶ generalization	▶ mathematical proof
▶ counterexample	▶ geometric sequence	▶ metacognition
▶ deductive reasoning	▶ Harshad numbers	▶ recursive rule
▶ explicit rule	▶ inductive reasoning	▶ triangular numbers

Study Guide

Mathematical Reasoning

Part 1. What did you learn?

1. Imagine that your uncle asks you what you have been studying in math class.

   a. Explain the difference between inductive and deductive reasoning.

   b. Give him examples that show when it is appropriate for a mathematician to use inductive reasoning and when it is appropriate for a mathematician to use deductive reasoning.

   c. Discuss the advantages and disadvantages of each type of reasoning.

2. Sonja says that if an integer is divisible by 3 and 6, it is also divisible by 18. Find a counterexample to her generalization.

3. For the table below, give the missing numbers or expressions. First, find the recursive rule and then use this to help you find the explicit rule.

Term	-6	-4	-1	0	1	2	3	7	9	14	n
Value		-22	-7		3	8		33	43		

4. What is the difference between a recursive rule and an explicit rule?

5. a. Prove that the sum of three even numbers is always even.

   - Let $2a$ represent one even number, $2b$ represent another even number, and $2c$ a third even number.

   - Using the distributive property, $2a + 2b + 2c = 2($ _____ + _____ + _____ $)$.

   - $2(a + b + c)$ is even. This is true because _____ .

   - Therefore, the sum of any three even numbers is _____ .

   b. What type of reasoning did you use in Part a?

6. For each of the following sequences, find the next three terms. Tell whether the sequence is arithmetic or geometric.

   a. 4, 8, 12, …

   b. −288, −317, −346, …

   c. 16, 8, 4, …

   d. 64, 16, 4, 1, $\frac{1}{4}$, …

   e. 7, 35, 175, …

7. Tracy thinks that multiplying a number by 2 is the same as squaring the number because $2 \cdot 2 = 2^2$. Give a counterexample to disprove Tracy's statement.

8. Write a number riddle where the answer is 10. Use three or four clues.

9. Which type of reasoning, inductive or deductive, do you use to solve a number riddle?

10. Complete the following statement with the most logical conclusion: All parallelograms have two pairs of parallel sides. A square is a parallelogram so _____ .

   •This is an example of what type of reasoning?

11. Four friends, Cameron, Alex, Ella and Gordy, won the top four places in an art contest. They each entered with a different type of art work. There was a photograph, a painting, a sketch and a collage. For each person, use the clues below to find which place they took with what kind of art they made.

   • Neither the painting nor the sketch took first, but one of them took third.

   • The person in second place thought either Gordy or the collage should have taken the top prize though neither had.

   • Cameron congratulated everyone, even though Ella placed higher than him and Alex placed lower.

- Gordy's aunt bought him a new paint smock to congratulate him.

	Photo	Painting	Sketch	Collage	1st	2nd	3rd	4th
Cameron								
Alex								
Ella								
Gordy								
1st								
2nd								
3rd								
4th								

12. Create a table that has a recursive rule of "add four" and an explicit rule of "the term number times four minus one."

Part 2. What went wrong?

13. Stefi looked at the table below.

Term (t)	1	2	3	4	7	9	14	n
Value (v)	−3	−6	−9	−12				

She said that the explicit rule was $v = 3$ since "you subtract 3 each time." What is wrong with Stefi's reasoning? How could you help her correctly identify the explicit rule?

14. Ronnie looked at the first three triangular numbers (1, 3, 6). He thinks that the 4th triangular number is 9 since the pattern is "multiples of 3". What could you say/do to help Ronnie understand why his description of the pattern is incorrect?

The Pythagorean Theorem

In the next two sections, you will take on the role of surveyor. A surveyor's job involves measuring distances, directions and angles. In fact, geometry is a Greek word that means "measuring the earth," which is what surveyors do. As a surveyor, you will determine land boundaries, find distances across lakes, design bridge spans and map out a new community.

Surveyors need tools to help them take measurements. Today, surveyors use technology such as the Global Positioning System (GPS) and laptop computers. But surveyors didn't always have such technology.

Surveying with Right Triangles

Start It Off

Anaya and Isabel arranged six tiles into the two different patterns shown below. One has a perimeter of 10 units, and the other has a perimeter of 14 units.

Explain to them why it is possible to arrange the same number of tiles into figures with different perimeters. Is there an arrangement of six tiles that will give another perimeter?

The Palermo Stone

Surveying is a very old profession. The ancient Egyptians were clever mathematicians and good surveyors. Just take a look at the Egyptian pyramids to imagine the precision of the measurements they made, the creative tools they used, and the knowledge of mathematics they possessed.

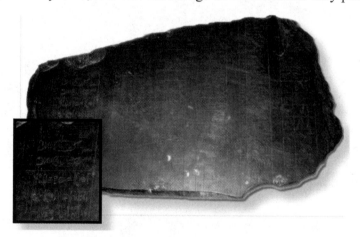

The Palermo Stone, above, dates to 2350 B.C. The stone lists the Egyptian kings and adds the most outstanding events of their reigns such as processions, festivals, and wars. It also includes records of the flood heights of the Nile River measured by Egyptian surveyors. Three heights are listed below.

3 cubits, 4 hands, 3 fingers

3 cubits, 5 hands, 2 fingers

2 cubits, 2 fingers

A cubit is a unit of measure the Egyptians used. One cubit measures the distance from a man's elbow to the tip of his longest finger.

1. Talk to your partner, answer the following. How many inches do you think are in a cubit? The Egyptians also used the units hand and finger. How do you think the Egyptians measured a hand? A finger?

2. Use an encyclopedia or the Internet to find the actual number of inches in a cubit, hand and finger.

In ancient Egypt, the Nile River overflowed every year. This changed the shape of the land near the river. Sometimes the stones that were boundary markers disappeared. Each year the surveyors made new boundaries, which involved measuring and marking off right angles. To do this, they invented a tool. It was a piece of rope with 13 equally-spaced knots placed 1 cubit apart. The length of the rope was 12 cubits. This tool actually helped them reestablish boundary lines by accurately measuring and marking off right angles.

 The Egyptians called the rope "the cord with 12 knots" even though it had 13 knots. Superstition required it!

The Royal Society of Harpedonapata

Surveyors held one of the most respected positions in Egyptian society. They were called, *harpedonapata,* or rope stretchers. They belonged to the Royal Society of Harpedonapata.

3. Imagine that you are a member of this society. You need to determine boundaries of rectangular tracts of land after the Nile has flooded.

   a) Discuss with your team members why finding right angles is important in making these boundaries.

   b) You will find right angles by making triangles. What type of triangle is needed?

Work like an Egyptian

Materials for each team:

  ▸ a rope with 13 knots, equally spaced

  ▸ Lesson Guide 2.1 *Joining the Royal Society of Harpedonapata*

  ▸ a protractor or index card to measure right angles.

Your Task

  • Work in teams of four.

  • Make triangles with the rope by selecting three knots and stretching the rope tightly between them. Three students should hold the rope firmly, with one student placed at each knot. The first and last knot should overlap to complete the triangle.

  • The fourth team member tests if the triangle has a right angle by using the protractor or index card.

4. Record the number of intervals between the knots on each side of the triangles you make.

Side 1	Side 2	Side 3	Right Triangle?

a) How many unique triangles can be formed with the rope?

b) Are any of these triangles right triangles? If so, what are the lengths of their sides?

c) If you could add more equally-spaced knots equally spaced on the rope, would it be possible to make more unique right triangles? If so, draw and record the lengths of the sides of one additional right triangle. How are the lengths of the sides of the new triangle related to the sides of the original triangle?

 **Hint**
See page 124

Creating New Boundaries

Imagine that a natural disaster has just happened where you live and has erased boundary marks. You find the marking of one edge of the boundary of your property. This is all that remains. You and your neighbors share a property that was divided into four equal rectangular parts. You agree with your neighbors to create a rectangular grid to map the property boundaries.

5. Your teacher will assign your team to a classroom "territory" where one piece of masking tape indicates one side of your property. You need to create the largest rectangular territory possible within the space you are assigned, given this one side.

 **rap It Up**

a) Can a right triangle have more than one right angle? Justify your answer.

b) What type of reasoning are you using—inductive or deductive? Explain.

MATHEMATICALLY
SPEAKING

▶ cubit

▶ finger

▶ hand

MATERIALS LIST

▶ Internet access

▶ Protractor and/or index card

▶ String or piece of yarn marked into 30 equal intervals

 **Write About It**

1. Why do you think the Egyptians used exactly 13 equally-spaced knots on their ropes?

2. Mark a string or piece of yarn into 30 equal intervals. Use this string to form five unique triangles. Draw and record the lengths of the sides of each triangle. Identify the right triangle and explain why it is a right triangle.

3. Using the measurements you found for the length of a cubit, hand and finger in Question 1, find the heights of the Nile River that were listed in the lesson.

4. Can a right triangle be isosceles? Can a right triangle be equilateral? Can a right triangle be scalene? If you answered yes to any of these questions, draw an example. If you answered no explain your reasoning.

 **Hint**
See page 124

5. Maria says she can draw a pentagon that has congruent sides and contains a right angle. Daren says this is impossible. Who is correct? Explain your reasoning.

6. Is there a convex polygon with congruent sides and right angles? Explain your answer with words and pictures.

 **Hint**
See page 124

 Think Beyond

7. In colonial days, surveyors used a tool called a Surveyor's Chain or Gunter's Chain. Research this tool using the Internet. How was this chain like the Egyptian rope? What was its primary purpose?

8. Find the perimeter.

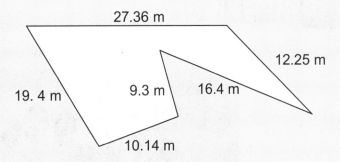

27.36 m

12.25 m

19. 4 m 9.3 m 16.4 m

10.14 m

9. Eighteen is twelve less than 5 times _____.

10. Cecilia has to mail a jewelry box that is in the shape of a 4-inch cube. Would she be able to pack it in the container below? Explain your answer. How much brown mailing paper would it take to cover the jewelry box (using no overlap of paper)?

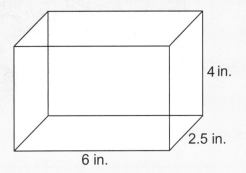

4 in.

2.5 in.

6 in.

11. If $x = 4$, then $3 + 5x =$

   A. 60   **C.** 23

   B. 32   **D.** 12

12. If Jackson has $3, he can buy 16 pencils. How many pencils can he buy if he has $24?

Patterns and Pythagoras

 **Start It Off**

The Mark family got together for the holidays.

1. **a)** Find the ratio of male adults to female adults in the photo.

   b) Find the ratio of children to adults.

   c) Find the ratio of adults to children.

2. The Vuolo family has the same ratio of children to adults as the Mark family, but the Vuolo family has 6 children. How many adults are in the Vuolo family? Explain your answer.

3. The Sheffield family has the same ratio of male adults to female adults as the Mark family. They have 32 men in their family. How many women are there? Explain your answer.

4. The Chapin family has 3 fewer women than men in their family. Their ratio of women to men is the same as the ratio in the Mark family. How many men and how many women do they have in their family? Explain your answer.

From the Egyptians to Pythagoras

Many different civilizations have been fascinated by right triangles.

Look at the picture of the Great Pyramid.

1. Talk to a partner and answer the following question: Where did the Egyptians use right triangles in the construction of this pyramid?

MATHEMATICALLY SPEAKING

▶ Pythagoras

The Greeks also knew about right triangles. One of the most famous and important geometric theorems is about right triangles. It was named after a Greek mathematician, Pythagoras.

Pythagoras was from Samos in Greece and lived from about 580 B.C.E (Before the Common Era) to 500 B.C.E. He traveled to Egypt and learned many of their surveying techniques including those of the rope stretchers. Pythagoras and his followers are the ones credited with proving a powerful theorem about right triangles. Today this theorem is used by surveyors, architects, engineers and carpenters in their daily work.

2. Like Pythagoras and his followers, you will now investigate right triangles and discover a new theorem. You will draw right triangles, record the lengths of the sides and the areas of the squares formed on the sides, and look for patterns.

a) On centimeter grid paper, draw a line segment that is 3 cm long. Then draw a 4 cm line segment that is perpendicular to the 3 cm segment. Draw the hypotenuse to form a right triangle. What is the length of the third side, in centimeters?

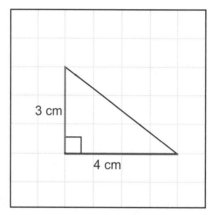

b) Cut out a square with sides of length 3 cm from centimeter grid paper. Write the area of the square inside it. Make two more squares whose sides are the same lengths as the other two sides of your triangle.

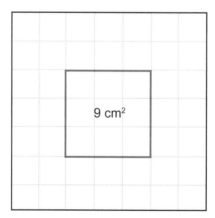

c) Place the squares on the sides of the triangle with corresponding lengths as shown.

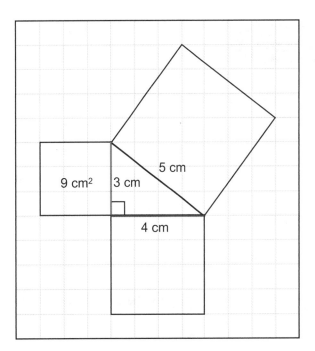

d) Complete the first row of the table.

Side a (in cm) (shortest)	Side b (in cm)	Side c (in cm) (longest)	Area of square on side a (cm²)	Area of square on side b (cm²)	Area of square on side c (cm²)
3	4	5	9		
6	8				
9	12				
5	12				
8	15				

3. Work in groups of four. Each member of the group should do the following for one row of the table:

 • Create a right triangle on centimeter grid paper with sides of lengths a and b forming the right angle in the triangle.

 • Label the third side of the triangle c.

 • Measure the length of the third side with a centimeter ruler.

 • Make squares with the same lengths as the three sides. Place the squares on the sides of the triangles.

 • Record findings in the table.

4. As a team, use inductive reasoning and look for patterns among the rows. What do you notice? Record all the patterns your group finds.

Whole numbers that are the lengths of the sides of a right triangle are called Pythagorean triples. For example, 3-4-5 is a Pythagorean triple.

5. Examine your table. What relationship did you find between the three sides of any right triangle?

    a) Use words to describe this relationship.

    b) Use variables and symbols to describe this relationship.

6. **a)** What pattern do you see as you look down the columns in the following chart?

Right Triangles		
Side a	Side b	Side c
3	4	5
6	8	10
9	12	15

    b) Extend the pattern in the table to find three new Pythagorean triples. Now, test if your new triangles fit the pattern you found in Question 4.

    c) Find the ratio of the sides in the second triangle to the corresponding sides in the first triangle. Find the ratio of the sides of the third triangle to the corresponding sides of the first triangle.

Wrap It Up

Just like Pythagoras, you have discovered an important relationship among the sides of right triangles. It is called the Pythagorean Theorem.

With a partner discuss the following:

a) Have you proven this theorem to be true? Explain your reasoning.

b) How could you show that the theorem was not true?

MATERIALS LIST

▶ Centimeter graph paper

▶ Rulers

 **Write About It**

1. **a)** Use words and a diagram to explain the Pythagorean Theorem to someone who does not know about it. Use good math vocabulary.

   b) Use symbols and the diagram you made in Part a to describe the theorem.

2. Does the equation $a^2 + b^2 = c^2$ hold for triangles that are *not* right triangles? On centimeter grid paper, make an equilateral triangle with sides of 5 centimeters each.

   a) Does the Pythagorean Theorem hold true for this equilateral triangle?

   b) Experiment with other equilateral triangles. Draw a conclusion.

3. Below are the lengths of sides of a few triangles.

   Does the Pythagorean Theorem hold for them?

   Can you make a right triangle on grid paper with these side lengths?

   a) 7-7-13   **c)** 4-4-5

   b) 5-6-9   **d)** 7-24-25

4. Miravalda said that the Pythagorean Theorem works for all scalene and right triangles. Do you agree with her? Explain your answer.

5. Find two new Pythagorean triples using the 5-12-13 triangle and the 8-15-17 triangle. Show that they fit the Pythagorean Theorem.

6. Malia says a triangle with side lengths 50 mm, 120 mm and 130 mm would be a right triangle. Show that she is correct without drawing the triangle.

   ? Hint
   See page 124

7. Staircases are based on a ratio of the length of the rise to the length of the tread. The Uniform Building Code (UBC) for spiral staircases says the rise should measure between 8.75 in. and 9.50 in. and the tread should measure 12 in. A builder uses the ratio of 3 : 4 for the length of the rise to the length of the tread.

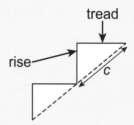

a) To meet the code using the ratio 3 : 4, what rise should the builder use? Explain your answer.

b) Find the length of c in the diagram, using the builder's rise and tread measurements. Explain how you found this.

**Hint**
See page 124

c) Measure a step on a staircase where you live. What is the ratio of the rise length to the tread length? Does it fit the builders' ratio of 3 : 4? Why or why not?

Think Beyond

8. Look up the definition of similar triangles. Will triangles whose sides are Pythagorean triples always be similar triangles? Why or why not?

Think Beyond

9. The Pythagorean triples 3-4-5, 5-12-13, and 8-15-17 are called primitive Pythagorean triples. This is because the numbers for the three side lengths are relatively prime.

a) What do you think the term "relatively prime" means? Check in a mathematics dictionary to see if you were correct.

b) There are 16 primitive Pythagorean triples where c is less than 100. Find three more sets.

Think Beyond

10. Find out more about Pythagoras and report back to the class some new interesting information. Here are two websites to get you started.
http://www.arcytech.org/java/pythagoras/history.html
http://www-groups.dcs.st-and.ac.uk/~history/Biographies/
Pythagoras.html

11. Find the area of the square and the pentagon.

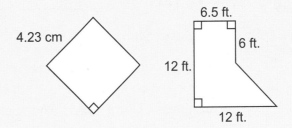

12. The area of the trapezoid is 324 square units. Find its height. Show your work.

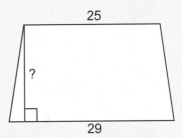

13. Fill in the missing terms in this arithmetic sequence:

    _____, 7, 13, 19, 25, _____.

    What is the recursive rule?

14. $4 - 7 + 3 - 1 =$

    A. -2 **C.** -7

    B. -1 **D.** -5

15. **What Went Wrong?**

    $104 = 130\%$ of _____?

    To solve this problem, Ariel found 30% of 104, 31.2. She then added $104 + 31.2$ to get 135.2. What did she do wrong?

Proving the Discovery

Start It Off

Egyptian Stone Designs

Imagine you are helping build an Egyptian Pyramid and have been asked to create a stone tile design that will be placed on the floor in one of the inner chambers of the pyramid. The stones you can use are shown below in the large square. The stones have been drawn to scale on the Lesson Guide that you should use to answer the questions below.

The area of the small triangle is 1 square unit.

1. What is the area of each of the other stone tiles?

2. What is the total area of the design?

Same Tiles, New Look

1. Cut out each stone tile from the Egyptian Stone Design Lesson Guide you used in the Start It Off. Use five to seven tiles and create a tile design for the pyramid chamber. What is the area of your design?

2. **a)** Use the same tiles you used in Question 1 and create a different design for the chamber. Compare the area of this design to your first design.

   b) If you use the same tiles to create a third design, what do you think the area will be? Explain.

Mathematical Theorems

MATHEMATICALLY SPEAKING

▶ conjecture
▶ theorem

When you look for patterns and make a discovery that seems to be true, this is called a conjecture. Think of it as an educated guess. Mathematicians try to prove that conjectures are true for every case.

When a conjecture is proven, it is called a theorem. In other words, a theorem is a general mathematical statement that has been proven true. Believe it or not, so far over 300 different ways have been found to prove the Pythagorean Theorem. Some of the authors of these proofs are surprising. For example Leonardo da Vinci (1452–1519) and President Garfield (1831–1881) each wrote a proof for the Pythagorean Theorem.

Proving the Pythagorean Theorem

Let's prove the discovery that you made in Lesson 2.2. This proof will justify calling it the Pythagorean *Theorem*.

 **Let's Review**   The sides of a right triangle have special names.

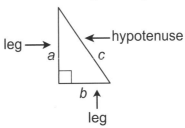

The Pythagorean Theorem states that the sum of the squares of the lengths of the two legs of any right triangle is equal to the square of the length of the hypotenuse. In a right triangle, this can be stated by the equation $a^2 + b^2 = c^2$, using the symbols in the diagram above.

To prove the Pythagorean Theorem you are going to put together a puzzle, using the following steps. This proof applies to all right triangles, so the lengths of the sides are not important.

Step 1.   Draw a right triangle on a piece of unlined paper by drawing a right angle (use a protractor) and then extending the sides to lengths of your choice. Connect the sides by drawing the hypotenuse. Label the legs, a and b, and label the hypotenuse c.

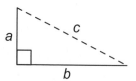

Step 2.   Draw squares on the three sides of the triangle as shown. Use a protractor to help you draw the right angles in the squares. Label the squares with their areas.

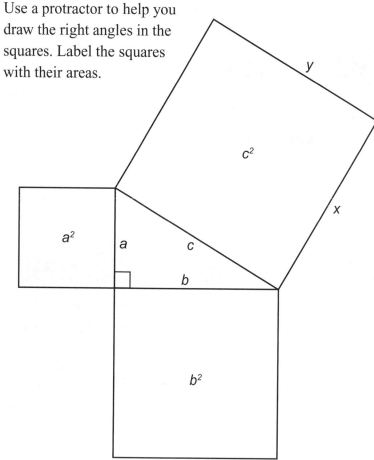

Step 3.   Find the center of the square with area b^2. (Think about how you should do this.) Mark the center of square b^2 with a dot.

 **Hint**
See page 124

Step 4. Label sides x and y of the square with area c^2 as shown below. Draw line segment 1 through your center dot in square b^2 parallel to side y of square c^2. Draw line segment 2 through the center dot parallel to side x of square c^2 as shown.

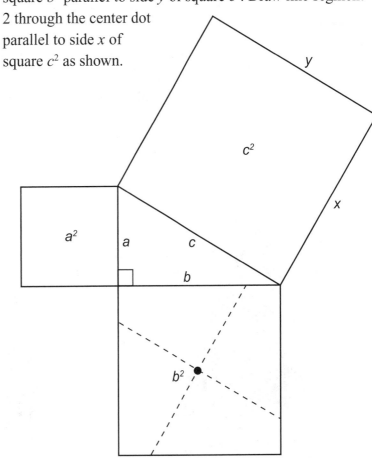

Step 5. Cut out square a^2. Cut square b^2 along the line segments you drew, so that you have 4 pieces. Now cover square c^2 completely with the five pieces (so $a^2 + b^2 = c^2$).

Step 6. Compare your right triangle to a different one used by another student. Were you both able to fit the smaller squares into the bigger one? What does this tell you?

Since these directions will work for **ALL** right triangles, the theorem is now proven.

This proof has been credited to Henry Perigal, a London stockbroker, and was published in 1873. It is a type of proof called a **dissection proof**.

3. Why do you think we call it a dissection proof?

4. Marianna is confused. She could not fit the squares a^2 and b^2 into square c^2. She told Leticia that you cannot cut up square b^2. She says that if you do this the area is not the same as the original square. Explain to Marianna why the area stays the same. Use the Egyptian Stone Designs to help you explain.

Marianna, Leticia, and Sophie were working on the dissection proof.

Explain why the area stays the same. Use the Egyptian Stone Designs to help you explain.

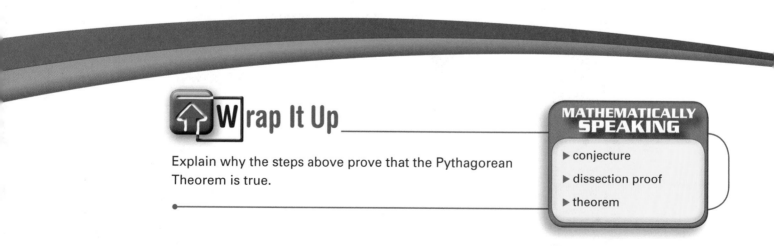

Wrap It Up

Explain why the steps above prove that the Pythagorean Theorem is true.

On Your Own

MATERIALS LIST

▸ Ruler

▸ Internet access

▸ Graph paper for **Think Beyond**

Write About It

1. How does the dissection proof of the Pythagorean Theorem show that it is true?

2. **a)** Explain the difference between a conjecture and a theorem.

    b) How are conjectures and theorems related to inductive and deductive reasoning?

3. Polly Gon has come up with a new conjecture. She knows that all rectangles are parallelograms and that all rectangles have 90° angles. She makes the conjecture that all parallelograms have 90° angles. Is Polly Gon's conjecture true or false? Justify your reasoning.

4. Put yourself in the place of Pythagoras. One day a colleague, Thales, is reading your journal and comes across your great new discovery. In the margin of one of the pages you have written $a^2 + b^2 = c^2$. Explain to Thales what your new discovery means.

5. Cal said the Pythagorean Theorem states that the square of the sum of the lengths of the legs of a right triangle equals the square of the hypotenuse. Using the side lengths of 3, 4, and 5 of a right triangle, show that Cal is incorrect.

6. Show that this triangle satisfies the Pythagorean Theorem.

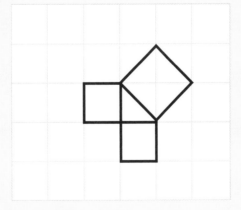

7. Go to illuminations.nctm.org/ActivityDetail.aspx?ID=30 on the Internet. The site has a visual proof of the Pythagorean Theorem that uses no words! How does this actually prove the Pythagorean Theorem?

8. Show that an isosceles right triangle with legs of length 2 cm satisfies the Pythagorean Theorem.

9. a) To find the area of the isosceles trapezoid below, Tiffany divides the trapezoid into two right triangles that have the same area and a square. Find the area of the trapezoid using Tiffany's method.

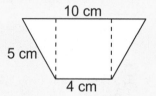

10 cm

5 cm

4 cm

b) Tony rearranged the isosceles trapezoid by moving one of the triangles to the other side. This made the figure into a rectangle. What is the length, width and area of the rectangle?

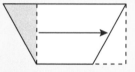

c) Compare the area of the rectangle and the area of the trapezoid. What do you notice? Why does this make sense?

10. Using the Internet, find out how President Garfield proved the Pythagorean Theorem. Demonstrate the proof for the class.

11. Evaluate the expression. Show each step in your computation.
    $[10 \cdot 9 - (8 + 7 \cdot 6)]$

12. One half of five more than thirteen is _____.

13. I have 8 short sleeve shirts, 6 long sleeve shirts, 4 pairs of pants and 10 pairs of socks.

    a) What is the ratio of short sleeves shirts to all the items of clothing? (One pair of socks counts as one item of clothing.)

    b) What is the ratio of shirts to pants?

    c) What is the ratio of short sleeve shirts to long sleeve shirts?

    d) What is the ratio of pants to all the items of clothing? Simplify when possible.

    e) If I buy six more long sleeve shirts and want to keep the ratios the same, how many short sleeve shirts should I buy?

14. What is the distance from $^-5$ to 8.5?

    A. 3.5   C. 14.5

    B. 8.0   D. 13.5

15. Sue Min says that every square is also a rectangle and a rhomus. Huong Ho disagrees. He says, "A square is also a rectangle because they both have right angles. But it is definitely not a rhombus, because a rhombus is slanted and so it can't have right angles." What do you think? Defend your position.

Optional Technology Lesson for this section available in your eBook

Sum It Up

In this section, you learned how Egyptian surveyors used right triangles to determine boundaries. You learned about the relationships among the lengths of sides in right triangles. You proved that this relationship holds true for all right triangles and is called the Pythagorean Theorem. The following are important mathematical ideas:

- The Pythagorean Theorem states that the sum of the squares of the lengths of the legs of a right triangle is equal to the square of the length of the hypotenuse. We proved this using a dissection proof.

- If you multiply all the side lengths of a right triangle by the same number, you get the side lengths of another right triangle. These side lengths are called Pythagorean triples. For example, a triangle with sides 3-4-5 is a right triangle. So triangles whose sides are 6-8-10 and 9-12-15 are also right triangles. Triangles with sides that are multiples of 5-12-13 and 8-15-17 are also right triangles.

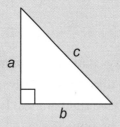

In this right triangle, $a^2 + b^2 = c^2$.

MATHEMATICALLY SPEAKING

Do you know what these mathematical terms mean?

▶ conjecture	▶ finger	▶ Pythagorean triples
▶ cubit	▶ hand	▶ theorem
▶ dissection proof	▶ Pythagoras	

Study Guide

The Pythagorean Theorem

Part 1. What did you learn?

1. Meno is confused about the Pythagorean Theorem. He asks, "Does it mean that, for any triangle, the sum of the squares of any two sides is equal to the square of the third side?" Give Meno the correct interpretation of the Pythagorean Theorem. Explain using pictures, words and/or symbols.

2. Piper used a 60-inch-long piece of rope with knots equally spaced to create a right triangle. If she used the entire length of the rope and selected three knots to be the three vertices of the triangle, what could be the side lengths of her triangle?

3. Explain the difference between a conjecture and a theorem.

4. Explain two ways to find each of the missing side lengths below. If you cannot find the length, explain why not.

a.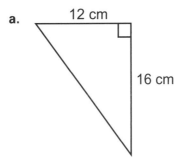
12 cm
16 cm

b.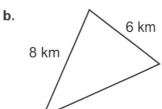
6 km
8 km

c.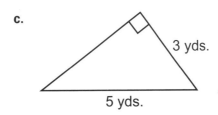
3 yds.
5 yds.

5. Kyle had the problem below on a recent quiz.

    > The length of a diagonal of a rectangle is 17 units. Its perimeter is 46 units. What are the dimensions of the rectangle?
    >
    > **A.** 23 by 23 units   **C.** 8 by 15 units
    >
    > **B.** 10 by 13 units   **D.** 17 by 29 units

    He chose answer B, but his answer was marked wrong. What could you do or say to help Kyle see why his answer was incorrect and help him find the right answer?

6. Hilding tried to find the area of square X in the diagram below.

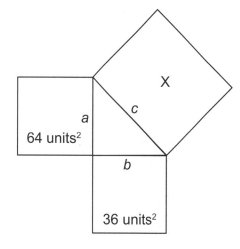

    Here is his work:

    $a^2 + b^2 = c^2$

    $36^2 + 64^2 = c^2$

    $1296 + 4096 = 5392$

    Hilding's teacher marked his answer wrong. Why? Where is the error in his method?

Using the Pythagorean Theorem

In this section, you will work with the Pythagorean Theorem. You will learn about the converse of a statement and the converse of the Pythagorean Theorem. You will also discover a set of numbers called irrational numbers.

Squares and Square Roots

Start It Off

▶ inverse operations

Addition and subtraction are inverse operations. This means that one operation undoes the other.

For example, $16.8 + 27.6 = 44.4$.

So, $44.4 - 27.6 = 16.8$ and $44.4 - 16.8 = 27.6$.

1. What is the inverse of multiplication? Give an example to illustrate.

2. For each of the following, write a statement to show the inverse operation.

   a) $\frac{3}{4} + \frac{1}{2} = $ _____

   b) $\frac{3}{4}\left(-\frac{1}{2}\right) = $ _____

   c) $-315 \cdot $ _____ $= 3,150$

   d) $68.4 \div 3.6 = $ _____

Inverse Operations

 Let's Review When we take the square root of a number, we do the opposite of squaring. This means we find a new number that when multiplied by itself equals the original number. We know $6^2 = 36$ and $(-6)^2 = 36$. Therefore, the square roots of 36 are 6 and -6.

For non-negative numbers, squaring a number greater than or equal to zero and taking the square root are *inverse operations*. This is because one undoes the other.

NOTE The principal square root of a number is the *positive* square root. It is written using the square root symbol $\sqrt{}$. For example, $\sqrt{36} = 6$. Here is a visual model.

6 cm | Area = 36 cm²

6 cm

To find the area of a square, you square the sides. The area of the square above is $(6 \text{ cm})^2 = 36 \text{ cm}^2$. To find the length of one side of the square, find the square root of its area, $\sqrt{36 \text{ cm}^2} = 6 \text{ cm}$.

1. Fill in the blanks with positive numbers. Then, write a mathematical statement to show the inverse operation.

   a) $24^2 =$ _____

   b) $1.5^2 =$ _____

   c) _____$^2 = 256$

   d) ____$^2 = 0.0009$

   e) $\sqrt{81} =$ _____

   f) $\sqrt{121} =$ _____

2. Use square roots to find the value of x.

   a) $x^2 = 289$

   b) $\sqrt{144} = x$

   c) $\sqrt{7 \cdot 7} = x$

   d) $\sqrt{169} - \sqrt{196} = x$

   e) $\sqrt{81} \div \sqrt{324} = x$

   f) $\sqrt{x} = 11$

   g) $x^2 = \dfrac{9}{16}$

   h) $\sqrt{\dfrac{81}{100}} = x$

   i) $x^2 = 0.09$

   j) $\sqrt{2.25} = x$

3. The area of a square piece of paper is 9.61 square inches. Make a conjecture about each of the following:

a) Will this sheet of paper lay flat on the bottom of a shoebox without being folded? Why or why not?

b) Will it lay flat on the inside bottom of a tall rectangular tissue box? Why or why not?

c) Will it lay flat inside a small jewelry box for a ring? Why or why not?

d) Find the actual length of a side of the piece of paper without a calculator.

Square Roots and the Pythagorean Theorem

To find the length of c in the right triangle, we use the Pythagorean Theorem.

$a^2 + b^2 = c^2$

$9^2 + 12^2 = c^2$

$81 + 144 = c^2$

$225 = c^2$

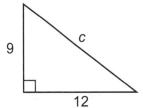

To undo the squaring of c, we have to take the square root. Remember, to solve an equation, you must perform the same operation on *both* sides of the equation.

Take the square root of both sides to find the value of c.

15 or $^-15 = c$

So the length of side c is 15.

4. Why don't we use the value $^-15$?

5. When possible, use the Pythagorean Theorem to find the missing side lengths.

a)

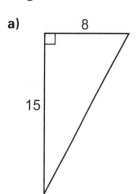

c)

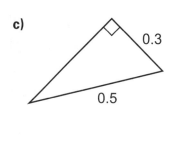

b)

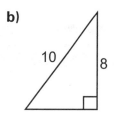

d)

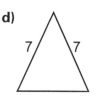

Building with the Pythagorean Theorem

In Question 7 on page 66, we discussed staircase designs. Find the right triangles in the diagram of the steps.

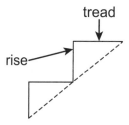

When building a house, sometimes stairs are in place before the work is finished. To bring supplies to the next level in a wheelbarrow, a builder puts a ramp over the stairs.

6. Assume there are 5 stairs going from a family room to a kitchen, with the rise of the step equal to 9 inches and the tread equal to 12 inches. How long would the builder have to make a ramp to help move supplies? Show your work.

7. A builder needed to work on a window that was 15 feet from the ground. His ladder was 17 feet long. The house is 9 feet away from the garage. Will there be enough room for the ladder between the house and the garage? Assume that the ground is perpendicular to the house. Explain your answer.

The Converse of the Pythagorean Theorem

▶ converse

You can think of the converse of a statement as its reverse. To write the converse of a statement in if-then form, switch the statements following the "if" and "then."

— **Example** —

Statement: If a polygon is a square, then the polygon has four congruent angles and sides.

Converse: If a polygon has four congruent angles and sides, then the polygon is a square.

8. Write the converse of each statement. Determine whether the converse is true or false. If it is false, give a counterexample.

   a) If your pet is a cat, then your pet has a tail.

   b) If tomorrow is Monday, then yesterday was Sunday.

   c) If a polygon has four sides, then it is a quadrilateral.

   d) If a number is divisible by 8, then it is divisible by 4.

The Pythagorean Theorem states: If a triangle is a right triangle, then the sum of the squares of the lengths of the two legs equals the square of the length of the hypotenuse.

9. Write the converse of the Pythagorean Theorem.

10. Use the converse of the Pythagorean Theorem which, in fact, is a true statement, to determine if the following lengths form a right triangle. Explain your answer.

    a) 3 cm, 6 cm, 7 cm

    b) 7 in., 25 in., 24 in.

    c) 17 m, 8 m, 14 m

    d) 30 cm, 50 cm, 40 cm

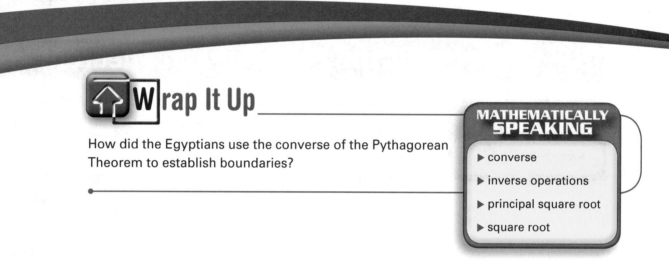

⬆W rap It Up

How did the Egyptians use the converse of the Pythagorean Theorem to establish boundaries?

MATHEMATICALLY SPEAKING

▸ converse

▸ inverse operations

▸ principal square root

▸ square root

LESSON
3.1

SECTION 3

On Your Own

MATERIALS LIST

▶ Internet access

Write About It

1. State the Pythagorean Theorem in words and using symbols. State the converse of the Pythagorean Theorem in words and using symbols.

2. The square numbers are 1, 4, 9, 16, 25, and so on. Why is this set of numbers called "the square numbers"? Find another interesting fact about square numbers. Be prepared to share your fact with the class.

3. Find the squares of the following numbers. Use parentheses and write an equation. Do not use a calculator.

   Example: Find the square of $\frac{2}{3}$
   $$\left(\frac{2}{3}\right)^2 = \frac{4}{9}$$

   a) 22

   b) 120

   c) 2.5

   d) $2\frac{3}{8}$

   e) 1.1

   f) 12.4

   g) $\frac{7}{100}$

4. Find the principal square root of each number. Use the square root symbol and write an equation. Do not use a calculator.

   Example: Find the principal square root of 100. $\sqrt{100} = 10$

   a) 1

   b) 169

   c) 1.69

   d) $\frac{64}{49}$

   e) $\frac{196}{400}$

Find the numerical value of the variable in each example below.

5.

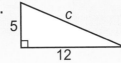

6.

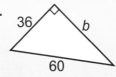

7.

8.

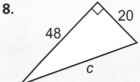

9. The bottom of a 13-foot ladder is 5 feet from a wall. How high up the wall will the ladder touch? Assume the ground is perpendicular to the wall. Draw a diagram and explain your answer.

10. a) The Carlsons are buying vertical blinds for their sliding door, pictured below. Walter from Valley Decorating and Design came to measure the window, and made the sketch below. He forgot to measure the slanted side. Can you help him? Explain your answer so he will understand the mathematics you use.

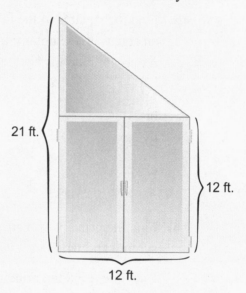

21 ft.

12 ft.

12 ft.

b) The Carlsons are also replacing the glass in their doors and window with ultraviolet-resistant panes. Using the outside dimensions of the door and the triangular window, find the maximum amount of glass they would need.

 Think Beyond

c) Can you figure out how much glass they need in a different way?

11. Park Rangers in Muir Woods in California have to use the skills of a surveyor. Ranger Forrest Stump is trying to find the height of a redwood tree that recently broke into two pieces. He measures the pieces of the tree and draws the following picture. Notice that one of the pieces is still attached to the trunk of the tree. Once he finishes drawing the picture he says, "I know the height of the tree."

 **Hint**

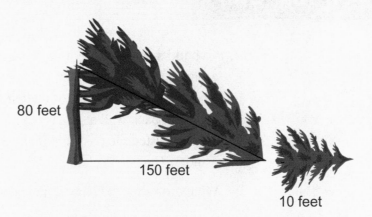

80 feet

150 feet

10 feet

a) How did he find the height? What was the height?

b) Do redwood trees really grow this tall? Find out about the giant coast redwoods in the Muir Woods Park. How tall can they grow?

12. Use the converse of the Pythagorean Theorem to determine if the following lengths form a right triangle. Explain your answer. Don't forget to use what you know about Pythagorean triples to make your work easier.

a) 10 m, 6 m, 8 m

d) 30 mm, 16 mm, 34 mm

b) 12 cm, 5 cm, 15 cm

e) 80 cm, 150 cm, 170 cm

c) 26 ft., 10 ft., 24 ft.

f) 30 m, 45 m, 75 m

13. To build a rectangular deck, Grace needed to make each angle a right angle. She did not have a protractor to measure the angle so she did what carpenters do to find out. For one corner, she measured the length (14 ft.), width (8 ft.), and diagonal (16 ft.) of the deck with a tape measure.

Does Grace have a right angle in the corner? Draw a picture, show your calculations, and explain your reasoning.

14. To build a garage in my backyard, the contractor drove a stake into the ground at the back corner ⒈. He put a second stake 9 feet along the line where I want a side wall of the garage to be ⒉. He then drove a stake along the back wall at 12 feet ⒊. He placed a rope between stakes 2 and 3. He adjusted the position of stake 3 until his rope fit perfectly between 2 and 3. Then he declared, "We're square."

What did he mean? How long was the rope that he brought?

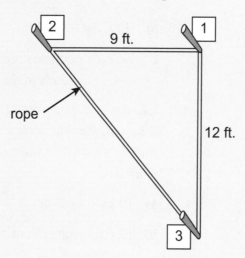

15. a) What type of triangle is formed when the sum of the squares of the lengths of the two shorter legs is less than the square of the length of the longest leg? Make a conjecture and then test it using a geometry software program such as Geometer's Sketchpad.

   b) What type of triangle is formed when the sum of the squares of the lengths of the two shorter legs is greater than the square of the length of the longest side? Make a conjecture and then test it using the geometry program.

Think Back

16. Which of the following is the least common multiple of 12 and 18?

    A. 6   **C.** 36

    B. 24   **D.** 216

    How did you get your answer?

17. If k can be replaced by any number, how many different values can $k + 6$ have?

    A. None   **D.** Seven

    B. One   **E.** Infinitely many

    C. Six

18. Estimate the value of the following. Then find the exact answer without a calculator. Was your estimate a good one? Why or why not?

    $37 + 3.7 + 0.37 + 0.037 =$

19. How much paper is needed to create a label for a soup can with height of 10 cm and diameter of 6 cm?

20. Find the missing numbers in the sequence: 1, $^-$2, _____, $^-$8, $^-$11, _____.

    What is the recursive rule?

The Real World and Messy Numbers

 **Start It Off**

1. Fill in the blanks with "all," "some," or "no."

   a) _____ whole numbers are integers.

   b) _____ fractions are integers.

   c) _____ integers are positive.

   d) There are _____ integers between $^-1$ and $^-2$.

   e) There are _____ integers between $^-1$ and $+1$.

2. a) Graph the following numbers on a number line.

   $$^-1.25, \quad 12\%, \quad \frac{0}{10}, \quad \pi, \quad 250\%, \quad \left(\frac{4}{8}\right)^2, \quad -\sqrt{16}$$

   b) Where did you put π? Why?

Perfect Squares Are Not So Perfect

MATHEMATICALLY SPEAKING

▶ perfect squares

Numbers that have integer values as their square roots are called perfect squares. For example, 4 is a perfect square since its principal square root is 2. However, in most cases, square roots of numbers are not integers.

3 ft.   3 ft.

c

Suppose you want to create a triangular garden. One leg of the triangle will run along the side of a house. The other leg will run along a fence that is perpendicular to the house. Both legs are 3 feet long.

You want to install edging along the slanted side of the garden. How much edging do you need?

Using the Pythagorean Theorem: $3^2 + 3^2 = 9 + 9 = 18$. So, $c^2 = \sqrt{18}$. There is no integer, that when multiplied by itself is equal to 18. So, $\sqrt{18}$ ft. is the length of the outside edge of the triangular garden. It is a real number that represents the length, but it is not an integer, nor a fraction for that matter. You can use a calculator to find an approximate value for $\sqrt{18}$: $\sqrt{18}$ ≈ 4.24. So, the length of the slanted side of the garden is about 4.24 feet. The exact length, however, is $\sqrt{18}$.

Meet the Pythagoreans

Pythagoras was a religious leader as well as a mathematician. He established a secret society whose members were called the Pythagoreans. The Pythagoreans refused to eat beans! And they were frightened of the number $\sqrt{2}$. In fact, they kept its discovery a secret and did not want the rest of the world to know about it.

1. Why do you think this is so? Discuss with your partner.

? Hint
See page 124

A meeting of the Pythagorean Society.

One of the Pythagoreans' important beliefs was that everything in the universe could be described with either whole numbers or fractions. These numbers are called . Rational numbers are all numbers that can be written as the ratio of two integers with the denominator not equal to zero.

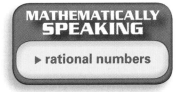

MATHEMATICALLY SPEAKING

▸ rational numbers

2. Common fractions suchs as $\frac{1}{2}$ are rational numbers. The Pythagoreans included integers as rational numbers. Do you agree with this? Explain your answer.

The Pythagoreans found that a right triangle could have legs with lengths of 1 unit. What was the length of the hypotenuse of this triangle? They knew that the hypotenuse squared had to be equal to 2. ($1^2 + 1^2 = 2 = c^2$).

3. The Pythagoreans were confused when they found that the hypotenuse squared was equal to 2. Why do you think this is the case? Talk with a partner about this.

Approximating $\sqrt{2}$

Let's take a look at the number $\sqrt{2}$.

4. Draw a right triangle on grid paper whose legs are each 1 unit in length. Draw squares on each side of the triangle. The area of each square on each leg is 1. What is the area of the square on the hypotenuse?

 **Hint**
See page 124

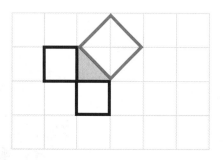

You should have found the area of this square to be 2 square units, which agrees with the Pythagorean Theorem ($1^2 + 1^2 = 2$). To find the length of the side, we take the square root of 2.

We can move the square to the number line to measure the length of its sides, one of which is the hypotenuse of the right triangle above. The length of the hypotenuse is a little less than 1.5. The value of the square root of 2 is 1.4142136... , a decimal that goes on forever with no repeating pattern of digits.

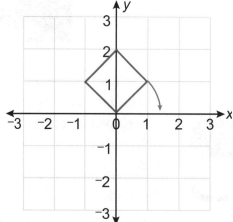

This is a real number, since it represents a length on the number line. But it is not a rational number since it cannot be written as a fraction. It is a decimal that never ends and does not have a repeating pattern.

Irrational Numbers

Irrational numbers are defined as real numbers that are not rational. They cannot be the form of a fraction, $\frac{a}{b}$ where $b \neq 0$ and a and b are integers. They are non-repeating and non-terminating decimals.

5. Why must $b \neq 0$ in the definition of an irrational numbers?

The Pythagoreans were so worried by the fact that $\sqrt{2}$ was not a rational number that they hid their discovery from the rest of their world. They preached that numbers explained the universe and now these numbers were behaving strangely! They called these numbers irrational numbers. They were the opposite of rational numbers.

MATHEMATICALLY SPEAKING

▶ **irrational numbers**
▶ **real numbers**
▶ **one-to-one correspondence**

6. **a)** Look up the definition of *irrational* in a dictionary. How does the definition of *irrational* in everyday language relate to the way the Pythagoreans viewed numbers?

We now know that irrational numbers are an important part of our number system, called the Real Number System. Irrational numbers are numbers that cannot be written as the ratio of two integers $\frac{a}{b}$ where b does not equal 0. ($\neq$). They are non-repeating and non-terminating decimals. Real numbers include rational and irrational numbers and make the number line a continuous line without any breaks. In other words, for every point on the number line, there is a number that corresponds to that point. We call this a one-to-one correspondence between numbers and points.

b) What number in the Start it Off was irrational? Explain.

7. Tell whether each number is rational or irrational. Justify each answer.

a)	-0.1	**e)**	0
b)	175%	**f)**	-819
c)	6.3401	**g)**	0.0000007
d)	$\sqrt{7}$	**h)**	$0.666666\ldots$

Square Roots and Irrational Numbers

Square roots of whole numbers that are not perfect squares, such as $\sqrt{7}$, are irrational numbers. You cannot find the exact value of such a number. However, you can find an approximation by using a calculator or by thinking about the two integers the number falls between on the number line.

For example, $\sqrt{7}$ is between 2 and 3 since $2^2 = 4$, $(\sqrt{7})^2 = 7$, and $3^2 = 9$.

8. Determine the two integers between which the following square roots lie.

   Here is an example: $\sqrt{24}$

   $\sqrt{16} = 4$ and $\sqrt{25} = 5$. Since 24 is between 16 and 25, $\sqrt{24}$ must have a value greater than 4 but less than 5. We write this as $4 < \sqrt{24} < 5$.

   a) $\sqrt{35}$

   b) $\sqrt{63}$

   c) $\sqrt{128}$

   d) $\sqrt{90}$

   e) $\sqrt{205}$

   f) $\sqrt{18}$ (Remember, this is the length of the border for the triangular garden in the problem shown previously.)

   g) Check your answers using a calculator.

Making Squares on the Geoboard

You can use your knowledge of squares and square roots and area to find the areas of all the different-sized squares on a Geoboard or dot paper.

9. Use 4-by-4 sections of dot paper to create as many different-sized squares as possible.

   a) How many squares did you find?

   Hint
   See page 124

   b) Work with a partner to compare your squares. See if together you can find all of them. Share your solutions with the class.

   c) Find the area of each square.

   d) Use the area of each square to find the length of the side of each square.

   Hint
   See page 124

Wrap It Up

How did irrational numbers first become known to the Pythagoreans?

How are irrational numbers different from rational numbers?

Why is the square root of a whole number that is not a perfect square irrational?

MATHEMATICALLY SPEAKING

▶ irrational numbers

▶ one-to-one correspondence

▶ perfect square

▶ rational numbers

▶ real numbers

LESSON
3.2   SECTION 3

On Your Own

MATERIALS LIST
▶ Calculator
▶ Graph paper

Write About It

1. What are rational numbers? What are irrational numbers? How do they differ? Give five examples of each.

2. Put the following numbers on a single number line. Tell whether each number is rational or irrational. Explain why.

   a) $-\sqrt{25}$ **f)** 0.5%

   b) $-2.26734\ldots$ **g)** 50%

   c) $\frac{17}{7}$ **h)** $1.758932\ldots$

   d) $\frac{0}{8}$ **i)** $\sqrt{49}$

   e) $-0.666\ldots$ **j)** $\sqrt{1.44}$

3. Decide if each number is rational or irrational. If the number is rational, write it in the form $\frac{a}{b}$, where a and b are integers and $b \neq 0$. If the number is irrational, find its decimal equivalent to the nearest hundredth. Indicate all the perfect squares.

   a) $\sqrt{729}$ **e)** $\sqrt{1000}$ **i)** 0

   b) $\sqrt{\frac{1}{4}}$ **f)** $0.33333\ldots$ **j)** $-\sqrt{100}$

   c) $\sqrt{112}$ **g)** $\sqrt{6.25}$ **k)** $-\sqrt{500}$

   d) -0.3451 **h)** $8.72398437560\ldots$ **l)** 128%

4. In the triangles below, find the value of the variable. First estimate its value by finding the two integers it falls between. Then find an approximation to the nearest hundredth using a calculator.

   Example:

   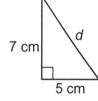

   $7^2 + 5^2 = d^2$

   $49 + 25 = d^2$

   Next, estimate the value of $\sqrt{74}$ by finding the two integers it falls between. $\sqrt{74}$ falls between 8 and 9 since $8^2 = 64$ and $9^2 = 81$. To the nearest hundredth, $\sqrt{74} \approx 8.60$

a)

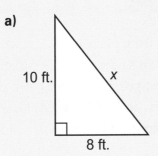

10 ft.   *x*

8 ft.

b)

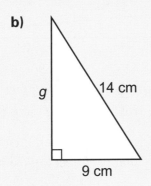

g   14 cm

9 cm

d)

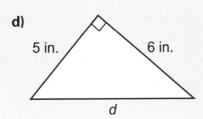

5 in.   6 in.

d

5. To the nearest thousandth, find the length of a side of a square whose area is 20 square inches. Explain how you found your solution.

6. a) An isosceles right triangle's legs measure 2 ft. To the nearest hundredth, find the length of the triangle's hypotenuse.

    b) A square has a side length equal to the hypotenuse of the triangle in Part a. Find the area of the square in two ways: using grid paper, draw a square on the hypotenuse side of the isosceles right triangle; and use the Pythagorean Theorem.

Hint
See page 124

7. To the nearest hundredth find the length of a side of a square whose diagonal is 34 centimeters. Explain how you found your solution.

8. Your surveying team plans to build a wheelchair ramp for a gym. This gym is being built so the Cruisers basketball team, a wheelchair team that plays in the Special Olympics, can practice and play games there. The Americans with Disabilities Act Accessibility Guidelines state that for every inch that the ramp rises it must cover 12 inches or 1 foot of ground.

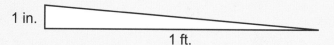

1 in.

1 ft.

The height of the ramp needs to be 2 feet. To the nearest hundredth of a foot, how much ground must the ramp cover?

9. Skyler and Navia need to move a circular tabletop that is 14 feet wide through a doorway that is 10 feet high and 7 feet wide. Can this be done? Explain.

10. You are going to build an entertainment center for your new TV. The screen diagonal of the TV is 22 inches. (This is the usual measurement given when purchasing a television.) There is a 3-inch border surrounding the screen. The height of the screen of the TV is 12.5 inches. If you build a cabinet that is 24 inches square, will it be big enough for the TV? Explain your answer.

11. Your surveying crew is working on a new project. You have to find the length of the embankments under a road bridge that crosses a highway. The height of the underpass must be tall enough to allow trucks and RV's to pass underneath and has been set at 22 feet. The span of the bridge is 40 feet to allow for two lanes of traffic (24 feet) and identical embankments on each side. Find the length (l) of the embankments to the nearest hundredth of a foot.

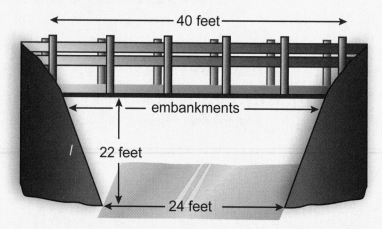

40 feet

embankments

22 feet

24 feet

Think Beyond

12. Create a Venn Diagram where the Universal set is the real numbers. Create circles for the rational numbers, irrational numbers, integers, whole numbers and natural numbers in your diagram.

Think Beyond

13. An irrational number cannot be written as a fraction. This is because its decimal representation is non-terminating and non-repeating. Non-terminating decimals that do repeat—such as 0.6666… and 0.27272…— are rational. This means you can write them as a fractions with integer numerators and denominators. How is this possible?

Mathematicians turn repeating decimals into fractions, using algebra.

For example, to write 0.6666… as a fraction, first write the equation, $n = 0.6666....$

Then multiply both sides of this equation by 10, $10n = 6.6666...$

Now subtract the original equation from this new equation.

$$\begin{array}{r} 10n = 6.6666 \\ -\ 1n = -0.6666 \\ \hline 9n = 6 \end{array}$$

Divide both sides of the difference by 9 to get $n = \frac{6}{9}$, or $\frac{2}{3}$. So 0.6666… is equal to $\frac{2}{3}$, a rational number.

Change the following repeating decimals to fractions.

a) 0.3333…

b) 0.1111…

c) 0.7777…

d) What pattern do you notice between a decimal that has a single repeating number and its fraction equivalent?

e) Predict what the repeating decimal is for the fraction $\frac{5}{9}$. Now find the actual decimal. Are you correct?

Write the fractions for the following repeating decimals:

f) 0.454545…

g) 3.156156156…

Think Back

14. **What went wrong?**

   Elizabeth evaluated $x(3 + 7(x - 4))$ for $x = {}^-2$, and got:

   $$^-2(3 + 7(^-2 - 4)) = {}^-2(3 + 7(^-6))$$
   $$= {}^-2(10(^-6))$$
   $$= {}^-2(^-60)$$
   $$= 120$$

   Her teacher said this was not correct. What went wrong?

15. Find the missing terms in the arithmetic sequence:

   _____, 4, 7, 10, 13, _____, _____.

   What is the explicit rule for the nth term?

16. What is the distance between $+8.2$ and $^-3.6$ on the number line? What number is half way between these two numbers?

17. Johanna and Josh are discussing a card game. In the game, you need to get four cards with the same number or face or four cards of the same suit. Johanna thinks you are more likely to get four cards with the same number or face (for example, 4 fives or 4 queens) than four cards of the same suit. Josh disagrees. Is Johanna or Josh correct?

   Explain your reasoning.

18. Explain the difference between a proportion and a ratio. Give an example of each.

Going the Distance

Start It Off

Copy and fill in the Venn Diagram with the correct terms. Draw a corresponding shape in each area that has a star.

Use these terms: *quadrilaterals, rectangles, parallelograms, trapezoids, squares, rhombi*

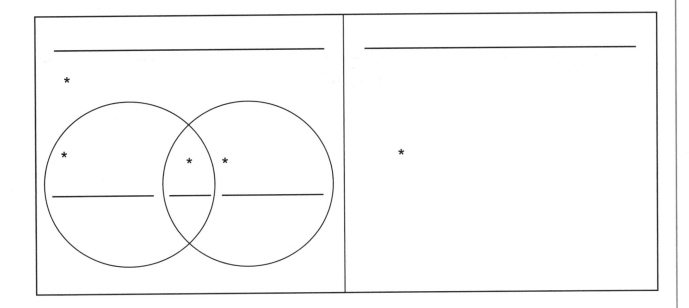

Compare your diagram with a partner's. Were your terms in the same place? Did you draw different shapes? Explain.

Find My Shape

1. We use coordinate systems to describe the locations in the real world. To review points on the coordinate plane, you are going to play **Find My Shape** with your partner.

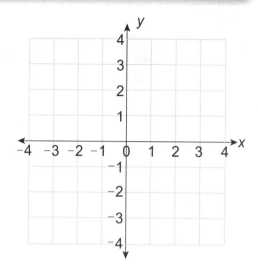

 · · · · · · · · **Find My Shape** · · · · · · · ·

Number of players: 2

Materials: A coordinate grid for each player

1. Without letting the other player see, draw a quadrilateral on the grid. Use a ruler to create straight lines and write the coordinates of the vertices. Make sure the vertices are on intersecting lines.

2. Tell the other player the name of the shape, being as specific as possible. Choose one of the following: square, rectangle, trapezoid, parallelogram. For example, if a shape is a square, you must say square and not rectangle or parallelogram. Then give the other player the coordinates of one of the vertices.

3. The other player must guess the other three vertices by naming the coordinates of the points.

4. After each guess, say:

   - "inside" if the point the player guessed falls inside the shape

   - "on" if the point is on the shape's border or vertex

   - "outside" if the point is outside the shape

5. The other player continues to guess until she finds all four vertices. Keep track of the number of guesses.

6. Now repeat these steps with the other player drawing the quadrilateral. The player who uses the least number of guesses to find all four vertices wins.

Planning a New Community

MATHEMATICALLY
SPEAKING

▶ plat

Did you know that Walt Disney was a surveyor? One of his first jobs was a draftsman in North Carolina where he prepared several subdivision plats that can be found in the county records. A plat is a blueprint for a plot of land. Maybe this is why Disney World is laid out so well!

Planning a new community requires the cooperation of many professionals, including land surveyors. The surveying team's responsibilities include establishing boundaries, designing streets and determining sewer line paths.

2. Your surveying team has just mapped the streets of a new community on the grid shown. Each unit represents 1 mile. Answer the following questions. Round your answers to the nearest hundredth.

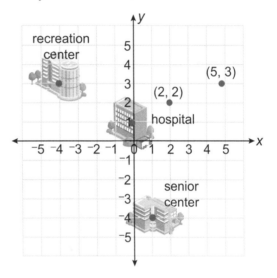

a) Name the coordinates of the recreation center, the hospital, and the senior center.

b) Find the shortest driving distance (which requires traveling along the lines of the grid that represent the streets) from the recreation center to the hospital. Explain how you arrived at your answer.

c) Perhaps you have heard of the phrase, "as the crow flies." This means the distance traveled if you could fly to a destination directly, with no obstacles in your way. Find the distance "as the crow flies" from the recreation center to the hospital. In what situation might this distance be used?

 **Hint**
See page 124

d) How much farther is it from the hospital to the senior center by car than if you were able to walk the shortest route without staying on the streets. Explain your reasoning.

e) Your surveying team needs to map out a new park in town. You have the following restrictions:

- The shape of the plot should be a right triangle.
- The endpoints of the hypotenuse are at (2, 2) and (5, 3).

What could the coordinates of the other point be? Discuss this with your partner. Is there more than one point that would work?

3. Add a middle school, a gas station, and a restaurant to the grid, and write down their coordinates. Make sure your new locations satisfy the following requirements:

a) The middle school is four blocks from the recreation center and six blocks from the hospital.

b) The shortest distance between the middle school and the restaurant is 5 miles.

c) The gas station is exactly halfway between the middle school and the recreation center.

d) Is there more than one possible location for any or all of the new places? Explain your answer.

Shapes on the Coordinate Grid

4. The Pythagorean Theorem can help you find lengths, perimeters and areas of shapes on the coordinate grid.

a) Find the lengths of each side of $\triangle ABC$ to the nearest hundredth.

Hint
See page 124

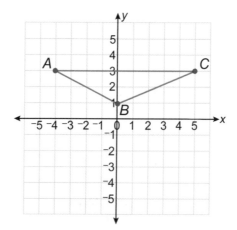

b) Find the perimeter of $\triangle ABC$ to the nearest hundredth.

c) Find the area of $\triangle ABC$.

5. Maya wonders why you use the Pythagorean Theorem to find the perimeter of △ABC but not its area. Explain why.

6. Draw a right triangle with a perimeter of exactly 12 units on a coordinate grid.

7. Use the Pythagorean Theorem to find the perimeter of the pentagon on the grid below.

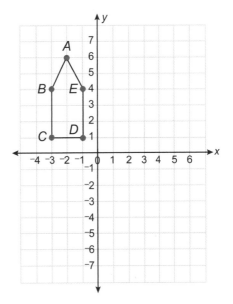

rap It Up_____

You are given two coordinates. Discuss the following with your partner.

a) How can you find the shortest driving distance between them?

b) How can you find the shortest distance between them as the crow flies?

c) How do you use the Pythagorean Theorem to find the shortest distance between two places "as the crow flies"?

Write About It

1. A right triangle's vertices have the coordinates $A\,(-4, -1)$, $B\,(-4, -4)$ and $C\,(-1, -4)$. How can you find the perimeter of the triangle using the Pythagorean Theorem? Draw a picture in your explanation.

2. In the lesson, you found more than one location for the park. Recommend to the town council one of these locations. Give specific reasons.

3. You are on a scavenger hunt and just received the following clues. The clues lead to a hidden treasure. Use grid paper to create a map based on the directions below.

   • From the stop sign at the top of Hill Street, walk 8 paces north.

   • Turn west and continue 15 paces.

   • Head north for 12 more paces.

   • Walk 9 paces west.

   Connect the starting point of the route to the ending point. The treasure will be $\frac{2}{3}$ of the way down this path. How many paces will you need to take down this path to find the treasure?

4. The French mathematician René Descartes (1596–1650) developed coordinate geometry, which is also called Cartesian geometry. There is a tale about how he came up with the idea of a coordinate system while he was sick in bed and noticed a fly on his ceiling. Research this on the Internet and summarize the story.

   Questions 5–7 ask about a ferry route across a lake.

5. A ferry route is being set up across Echo Lake from Compton (point C) to Derry (point D). You are hired to survey the property and find the distance across the lake that the ferry will travel. You are standing at a point E, directly west of Compton and directly south of Derry. From your point to Compton is 14 miles. From your point to Derry is 10.5 miles.

   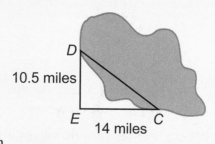

   a) Find the distance the ferry will travel.

   b) Explain to the ferry captain how you arrived at your answer.

6. If the ferry can travel 27 miles per hour, how long will it take to make the trip?

Hint
See page 124

7. The ferry captain plans to work from 8 am to 4 pm with stops on either side of the lake for 10 minutes. How many trips can she make in one day?

8. Use the Pythagorean Theorem to find the perimeter and area of each of the shapes below. Round lengths to the nearest hundredth. Show your work.

a)

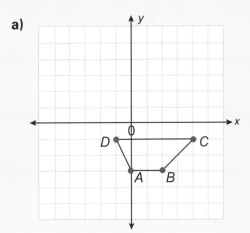

b)

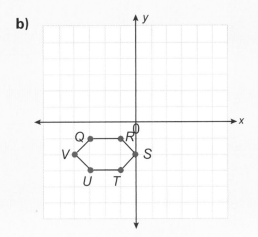

9. Find the perimeter of an octagon that has vertices at the following points: $A(-2, 0)$, $B(-1, 0)$, $C(0, -1)$, $D(0, -2)$, $E(-1, -3)$, $F(-2, -3)$, $G(-3, -2)$, and $H(-3, -1)$.

Round lengths to the nearest hundredth.

Think Beyond

10. The coordinates of two points on a coordinate system are given by (x^1, y^1) and (x^2, y^2). Show that the distance between these points can be represented by $\sqrt{(x_2 - x_1)^2 + (y_2 - y_1)^2}$. This is called the distance formula.

Think Beyond

11. Find the surface area and volume of the triangular prism whose front and bottom views are shown on the grid below using the distance formula. Round lengths to the nearest hundredth.

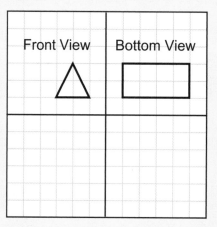

12. Evaluate $5\frac{1}{2} \div \frac{3}{4} \cdot \frac{2}{9}$. Is your answer rational or irrational? Explain.

13. **What Went Wrong?**

    Roberto had to do this calculation: $1.2 \cdot 0.11$.

    He set the problem up like this:

    $$
    \begin{array}{r}
    1.20 \\
    \times\ 0.11 \\
    \hline
    120 \\
    +\ 1200 \\
    \hline
    13.20
    \end{array}
    $$

    What went wrong?

14. How many square inches are in 2 square feet? How do you know? How is this different from 2 feet squared?

15. The product of a number n and 3 is 21. Which of the following represents this statement?

    A. $\frac{n}{3} = 21$ **C.** $n + 3 = 21$

    B. $n - 3 = 21$ **D.** $3n = 21$

16. Below is the base of Maria's perfume bottle. The shape of the base of the bottle is a rectangle with semi-circles on each end. Use 3.14 for π.

    a) If she wants to put a ribbon around the bottle, how much ribbon should she buy? Assume she needs 5 cm of the ribbon to make a bow.

    b) What area does the bottle take up on her bureau? Round your answer to the nearest hundredth.

    c) The perfume bottle is 10 cm tall with a top that is congruent to the base. What is the volume of the bottle?

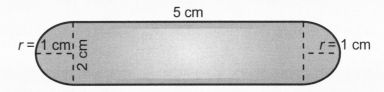

Optional Technology Lesson for this section available in your eBook

Sum It Up

In this section, you learned about the converse of the Pythagorean Theorem and used the theorem and its converse to solve a variety of problems. The important ideas from this section are:

■ The square root of a number is a number that, when squared, is equal to the original number. Positive real numbers have two square roots. For example, the square roots of 100 are 10 and −10.

■ The principal square root of a number is its positive square root. It is written using the square root symbol. Example: $\sqrt{225} = 15$.

■ For numbers greater than or equal to zero, squaring and taking the principal square root are inverse operations. For example, $10^2 = 10$ and $\sqrt{100} = 10$.

■ The converse of a statement is its reverse. To write the converse of a statement that is in if-then form, switch the statements following the "if" and "then." For example, the converse of the statement "If a polygon has three angles, it is a triangle" is "If a polygon is a triangle, then it has three angles."

■ The converse of the Pythagorean Theorem states that if the sum of the squares of the lengths of the shorter sides of a triangle is equal to the square of the length of the longer side, then the triangle is a right triangle.

■ Perfect squares are numbers that have integer values as their square roots. For example, 144 is a perfect square since its square roots are 12 and −12.

■ Irrational numbers are numbers that cannot be written as fractions. They are non-terminating and non-repeating decimals. The real number system is made up of rational and irrational numbers. For example, $\sqrt{2}$ and π are irrational numbers.

■ The Pythagorean Theorem can be used to find the shortest distance between two points on a coordinate system.

MATHEMATICALLY SPEAKING

Do you know what these mathematical terms mean?

▶ converse   ▶ perfect square   ▶ rational numbers

▶ inverse operations   ▶ plat   ▶ real numbers

▶ irrational numbers   ▶ principal square root   ▶ square root

▶ one-to one correspondence

Study Guide

Using the Pythagorean Theorem

Part 1. What did you learn?

1. Imagine you are Pythagoras and have just discovered the relationships among the lengths of the sides of a right triangle. The Greek citizens could care less! None of them believe your discovery is very useful. Write a speech to deliver to the citizens explaining the importance of this discovery. Include diagrams and other visuals to enhance your argument.

2. Sketch and label the side lengths of a triangle whose hypotenuse is more than 12 units but less than 15 units. Find the measure of the hypotenuse of the triangle you sketched. First, express its length as a square root and then as a decimal approximation rounded to the nearest tenth.

3. Explain the difference between squaring 9 and taking the square root of 9.

4. Zeddy tied a tree sapling to a stake in the ground to help it stay upright as it grows. If he used 3 feet of ribbon between the sapling and the stake, and the stake was 2 feet from the base of the sapling, about how high up was the ribbon tied to the sapling?

5. Put the following numbers on a single number line. Tell whether each number is rational or irrational. Explain why.

   a. $\sqrt{49}$

   b. $\sqrt{\frac{150}{3}}$

   c. $8.767766777666\ldots$

   d. $\frac{80}{6}$

   e. $\sqrt{\frac{32}{2}}$

   f. $5.2222\ldots$

   g. $\frac{59}{4}$

   h. 13.7

   i. $\sqrt{169}$

6. Find the perimeter of the shape below. Round to the nearest tenth of a unit.

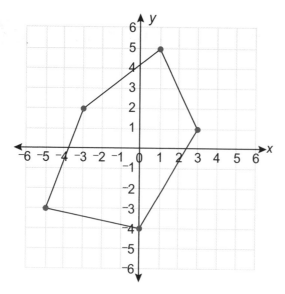

7. Locate two points on a coordinate grid that can be connected by a straight line whose distance is an irrational number. Calculate the distance of the line. Express your answer in two ways: as a square root and as a decimal approximation rounded to the nearest tenth.

Part 2. What went wrong?

8. Lydia thinks that a number can be rational or irrational depending on the way it is written. For example, she thinks that $\sqrt{64}$, $\sqrt{36}$ and $\sqrt{144}$ are irrational, but that 8, 6 and 12 are rational. What is wrong with Lydia's reasoning? How would you help her make sense of irrational numbers?

9. Carlotta likes to look at a right triangle and predict whether the measure of its hypotenuse will be rational or irrational. She looked at the right triangle below and said, "Its hypotenuse will be an irrational number because 8 plus 16 is 24 and the square root of 24 is an irrational number." Her friend Pete said, "Well, I agree that the hypotenuse will have a length that is irrational but not because of the reason you gave." What is the error in Carlotta's reasoning?

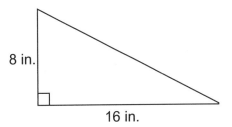

8 in.

16 in.

10. Lester had the question below on a test.

> **Which of the following expressions simplifies to an irrational number?**
>
> **A.** $\sqrt{64} - \sqrt{36}\sqrt{144}$
>
> **B.** $\sqrt{16} - \sqrt{2}$
>
> **C.** $\sqrt{4}\left(\sqrt{\frac{4}{16}}\right)$
>
> **D.** $\sqrt{4} - \dfrac{\sqrt{100}}{\sqrt{25}}$

He selected A, but his answer was marked wrong. What could you say to or show Lester to help him realize why his answer was incorrect and to find the correct answer?

Unit Study Guide

Prove It: Focusing on Mathematical Reasoning and the Pythagorean Theorem

Part 1. What did you learn?

SECTION 1

1. For the table below, give the missing numbers or expressions. Then, find the recursive rule and use it to help you find the explicit rule.

Term	1	2	3	4	7	9	14	n
Value	−2	−5	−8	−11				

2. Explain how to use inductive reasoning to find the explicit rule in the table in Question 1.

3. What is the difference between a recursive rule and an explicit rule?

4. All triangles have an interior angle sum of 180 degrees. An equilateral triangle has three equal angles. What is the measure of each angle? What type of reasoning are you using when you answer this question? How do you know?

5. Michael thinks that twice a number is always greater than the original number. Find a counterexample.

6. For each of the following sequences, find the next three terms. Tell whether the sequence is arithmetic or geometric and explain how you know.

   a. 7, 12, 17, ...

   b. 18, 9, 4.5, ...

   c. 17, 13.25, 9.5, ...

   d. 3, 12, 48, ...

23. Find the perimeter of the figure on the grid below as both an expression with a radical and as a number rounded to the nearest tenth.

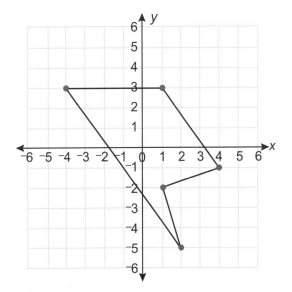

24. Locate four points that could be the vertices of a square whose area is 8 square units. Show or explain how you know the area is 8 square units.

Part 2. What went wrong?

25. Joao's teacher asked him to find the length of the hypotenuse of the right triangle pictured below. Joao said, "I added 4 and 6 and got 10. Then I squared 10 to get 100. This tells me c^2. So c is 10 because 10 is the square root of 100." Where is the error in Joao's method?

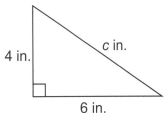

26. Luisa was asked to find the missing length of the base of the triangle pictured below.

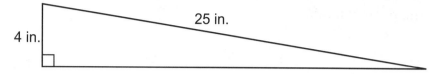

Here is her work:

$a^2 + b^2 = c^2$

$25 - 4^2 = 25 - 16 = 9$

$\sqrt{9} = 3$

She concluded that the length of the base was 3 inches. Where did Luisa go wrong? What would you do or say to help her correctly find the missing length?

27. Corey found the diagonal of a rectangle whose sides measure 7 cm and 10 cm. Here is his work:

$7^2 + 10^2 = 49 + 100$

$149 \div 2 = 74.5$

His teacher marked his answer wrong. Why?

arithmetic sequence A sequence with a constant difference between consecutive terms.

Example:

1, 3, 5, 7, ... The change between consecutive terms is +2.

10, 7, 4, 1, −2, ... The change between consecutive terms is −3.

conjecture When you look for patterns and make a discovery that seems to be true, this is called a conjecture. Think of it as an educated guess.

converse The result of reversing the statements following "if" and "then" in an if-then statement.

Example:

Statement: If a number C can be written as $\frac{a}{b}$ where a and b are integers ($b \neq 0$), then C is a rational number.

Converse: If C is a rational number, then it can be written as $\frac{a}{b}$ where a and b are integers ($b \neq 0$).

converse of the Pythagorean Theorem If the sum of the squares of the lengths of two sides of a triangle equals the square of the length of the third side, then the triangle is a right triangle.

counterexample An exception or contradiction to a proposed rule; an example where the rule does not work.

Example:

Given: Triangular numbers are 1, 1 + 2, 1 + 2 + 3, 1 + 2 + 3 + 4, ...

Proposed Rule: All triangular numbers are odd.

Counterexample: 6 is an even triangular number.

cubit An ancient measure representing the distance from a man's elbow to the tip of his longest finger (approximately 18 to 22 inches).

deductive reasoning A type of thought process used to make a specific conclusion from a set of existing facts or a generalization presumed as true.

Example:

Fact: All quadrilaterals have four sides.

Fact: A square is a quadrilateral.

Conclusion: A square has four sides.

dissection proof A proof based on cutting up (dissecting) and rearranging a figure using a geometric representation of the statement you are trying to prove.

Example:

See dissection proof of Pythagorean Theorem on page 68.

explicit rule A rule that provides an output value directly from the application of the rule on any input value.

Example:

Situation: I open a savings account with $10, and then deposit $50 each month.

Explicit Rule: $A = 10 + 50n$; A is the amount in account after n months of deposits.

exterior angle (of a triangle) The angle formed by one side of a triangle and an extension of an adjacent side.

Example:

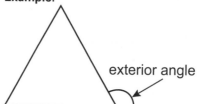

exterior angle

finger (or digit) An ancient measure representing the width of a man's finger, or one 28th of a cubit.

generalization A statement or rule applicable to every member of a group.

Example:

All quadrilaterals have four sides.

All rectangles are parallelograms.

geometric sequence A sequence in which each term is a constant multiple of the term preceding it.

Example:

2, 10, 50, 250, … Each term is 5 times the previous term.

-3, 6, -12, 24, … Each term is -2 times the previous term.

hand (or palm) An ancient measure representing the width of a man's hand or five fingers.

Harshad Number An integer divisible by the sum of its digits.

Example:

The sum of the digits of 18 is $1 + 8 = 9$ and $\frac{18}{9} = 2$.

The sum of the digits of 111 is $1 + 1 + 1 = 3$ and $\frac{111}{3} = 37$.

inductive reasoning A type of thought process used to arrive at a conclusion based on identifying and generalizing patterns in a set of observations.

Example:

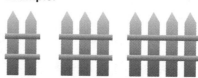

Observation:

Number of Sections	1	2	3	4	5
Number of Posts	2	3	4	5	6

Conclusion: A fence with n fence sections requires $n + 1$ fence posts.

interior angle (of a triangle) The angle formed by two adjacent (next to each other) sides in a triangle.

Example:

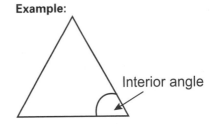

Interior angle

inverse operations Pairs of operations that undo each other.

Example:

Addition and subtraction: $8 + 6 = 14$ and $14 - 6 = 8$

Squaring a positive number and finding the principal square root: $9^2 = 81$ and $\sqrt{81} = 9$

irrational number A number that cannot be written as the ratio $\frac{a}{b}$ of two integers a and b, where $b \neq 0$.

Example:

$\sqrt{3}, \sqrt{2}, \pi$

mathematical proof A logical argument or demonstration that uses mathematical rules, properties and facts to show that a statement is necessarily true.

Example:

See proof on page 38.

metacognition The process of thinking about your own thinking and learning processes.

one-to-one correspondence The pairing of the members of two sets such that each member of the first set is paired with exactly one member of the second set, and each member of the second set is paired with exactly one member of the first set.

Example:

Set A: $\{1, 2, 3, 4, 5\}$ Set B: $\{1, 4, 9, 16, 25\}$

The set of integers 1 to 5 has a one-to-one correspondence with the set of their squares: $\{(1, 1), (2, 4), (3, 9), (4, 16), (5, 25)\}$.

perfect square A number that is the square of an integer.

Example:

$2^2 = 4$, $5^2 = 25$, $11^2 = 121$; 4, 25 and 121 are perfect squares.

plat A blueprint for a plot of land.

principal square root The positive result of the square root operation.

Example:

$\sqrt{25} = +5$, $\sqrt{144} = +12$, $\sqrt{2.25} = +1.5$

Pythagoras A Greek mathematician, philosopher and religious leader from the late 6th century BC credited with the discovery of the Pythagorean Theorem.

Pythagorean Theorem The theorem that relates the lengths of the three sides of a right triangle. It is formally written as: The area of the square built upon the hypotenuse of a right triangle is equal to the sum of the areas of the squares built upon the remaining sides. Stated another way, the sum of the squared lengths of the two shorter sides of a right triangle is equal to the squared length of the hypotenuse. In symbols, this is given a right triangle with sides of length a, b, and c, where c is the length of the hypotenuse, $a^2 + b^2 = c^2$.

Example:

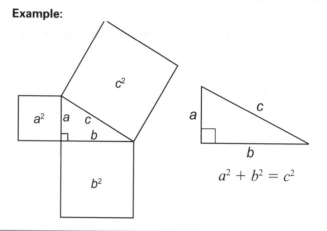

$$a^2 + b^2 = c^2$$

Pythagorean triple A set of three numbers $\{a, b, c\}$, often written as a-b-c, where $a^2 + b^2 = c^2$.

Example:

3-4-5, since $9 + 16 = 25$

5-12-13, since $25 + 144 = 169$

---

rational number A number that can be written as the ratio $\frac{a}{b}$ of two integers a and b where $b \neq 0$.

Example:

$3 = \frac{3}{1}$, $-5 = \frac{-5}{1}$, $0 = \frac{0}{1}$, $0.29 = \frac{29}{100}$, $0.\overline{3} = \frac{1}{3}$

---

real numbers The set of all rational and irrational numbers.

---

recursive rule A rule that uses result(s) of previous applications of itself in order to apply it again.

Example:

Situation: I open a savings account with $10 and deposit $50 each month. Therefore, each month my balance is $50 more than the previous month.

Recursive Rule: *new = previous + 50*; initial amount of $10.

---

square root (of a given number) A number that when multiplied by itself produces the given number.

Example:

The square root of 25 is either 5 or -5 since $(5 \cdot 5) = (-5 \cdot -5) = 25$.

The square root of 100 is 10 or -10.

The square root of 1.8769 is 1.37 or -1.37.

---

theorem A statement that has been proven to be true.

Example:

Pythagorean Theorem (see proof on page 67)

---

triangular numbers The numbers in the sequence where each term is the sum of the previous term and the term number: 1, 1 + 2, (1 + 2) + 3, (1 + 2 + 3) + 4, and so on. Geometrically, these are the number of "dots" required to form and fill in an equilateral triangle with sides of n dots.

Example:

Triangular Numbers: $\{1, 3, 6, 10, 15, 21, ...\}$

Lesson 1.1

Patterns with Pascal's Triangle

Page 4, Question 3d: A prime number has exactly two distinct factors: itself and 1. So 2 is a prime number; its factors are 1 and 2. 17 is a prime number; its factors are 17 and 1.

Page 4, Question 3e: Start with Row 1, which is the number 11. Row 2 is the number 121. How are these two numbers related?

Page 4, Question 3f: The row number, n, becomes an exponent when writing the sum of the numbers in Row n.

On Your Own

Page 9, Question 3: Make a two-column chart with with the headings "Number of Parallel Lines" and "Number of Regions" to help you.

Page 9, Question 5: Consider the number of diagonals that can be drawn from each vertex of an n-sided polygon to help you find the explicit rule.

Lesson 1.2

At School with Carl Gauss

Page 15, Question 3e: In the sum of the first consecutive 10 numbers, n is 10. So $11 = n + 1$. How many times did we add $n + 1$? To get the final answer, what do we need to divide by? Why?

Lesson 1.4

The Process of Elimination

Page 29, Question 2, Clue 2: Cross out all numbers that don't add to 15.

Page 29, Question 2, Clue 3: A palindrome is any number that reads the same backwards and forwards such as 121. Make a list of all possible numbers.

CAT SHOW

Page 31, Question 6:

	Gold	Silver	Bronze	Pewter	Yellow	Brown	Blue	Orange
Siamese					X	X	O	X
Tabby							X	
Persian							X	
Abyssinian							X	

	Gold
	Silver
	Bronze
	Pewter

On Your Own

Page 33, Question 3, Clue 1: Since there are so many possibilities, you should not list them all. Instead, think about what digits cannot be used in the hundreds place.

Page 33, Question 3, Clue 3: There is only one remaining possibility!

Lesson 1.5

On Your Own

Page 42, Question 3: Refer to the proof used in Page 43, Question 5 in the lesson. How can you use the distributive property to prove Jonas' hypothesis?

On Your Own

Page 43, Question 5: You need to determine the role of the woman in this situation.

Page 43, Question 6: Look back to Page 40, Question 5 in the lesson. What was the generalization about the sum of any two even numbers?

Page 43, Question 8a: Use n to represent any number and then perform the indicated operations on it.

Lesson 2.1

Work like an Egyptian
Page 55, Question 4c: Try putting two ropes together to make a longer rope and use this new rope to create a right triangle.

On Your Own
Page 56, Question 4: An isosceles triangle has two sides that are equal in measure. No two sides of a scalene triangle are equal in measure

Page 56, Question 6: In a convex polygon, each angle measures less than 180 degrees and each diagonal does not pass outside of the polygon.

Lesson 2.2

On Your Own
Page 63, Question 6: Look for equivalent ratios.

On Your Own
Page 64, Question 7b: A right angle is formed between the rise and the tread of each step.

Lesson 2.3

Proving the Pythagorean Theorem
Page 68, Step 3: Draw the diagonals of the square.

Lesson 3.1

On Your Own
Page 84, Question 11: The tree is perpendicular to the ground.

Lesson 3.2

Meet the Pythagoreans
Page 89, Question 1: How does this number differ from $\sqrt{4}$ or $\sqrt{9}$?

Approximating $\sqrt{2}$
Page 90, Question 4: Count the half-square units to determine the number of full square units that make up the area of the square.

Making Squares on the Geoboard
Page 93, Question 9a: You should be able to find a total of 8 different squares on dot paper.

Page 93, Question 9d: A side formed by connecting two dots on the dot paper does not necessarily mean that its length is 1 unit. Some distances between dots are longer than others.

On Your Own
Page 95, Question 6b: Use the graph paper to find the area by counting squares. Use the Pythagorean Theorem to find the square of the hypotenuse. How does this relate to the area of the square?

Lesson 3.3

Planning a New Community
Page 101, Question 2c: Think about how you can draw a right triangle and use the Pythagorean Theorem to help you find the distance.

Shapes on the Coordinate Grid
Page 102, Question 4a: Break the triangle up into two right triangles. Use the lengths of the base and height of the right triangles to find the lengths of two of the sides of the larger triangle.

On Your Own
Page 106, Question 6: Use the formula $d = rt$ (that is, distance = rate $\times$ time).

Index

V

value
   finding output using recursive rule 6

variables
   relating two using explicit rule 6

Venn diagram 97, 99